Teine Sāmoa

Dahlia Malaeulu

First paperback edition published in 2020

© Dahlia Malaeulu, 2020

Published by Dahlia Malaeulu

ISBN 978-0-473-52749-5

A catalogue record for this book is available from the National Library of New Zealand.

Teine Sāmoa Story Editor: Sue Copsey

Teine Sāmoa Project Editor: Donna Blabey & Dahlia Malaeulu

Gagana Sāmoa Translator: Niusila Faamanatu-Eteuati

Cover Design: Dahlia Malaeulu, Darcy Solia & Malo Gray

Cover Photographer: Anita Peniata

Cover Model: Azalia Le-Valasi Samasoni

For my mother, Lagimauga Gray, o 'oe le toa.

For all the Pasifika students I have ever taught at W.I.S.

For educators creating more brown spaces in our schools for our tamaiti.

For anyone who has ever questioned if they were a teine Sāmoa – this for us.

'E iloga le tama ma le teine Sāmoa i lana tu, savali, ma lana tautala'.

(A Sāmoan boy and girl is revealed by how they carry themselves, walk and how they speak.)

-     Sāmoan Proverb

CHAPTER 1

Lani Sio

I remember when I first met the 'Real Sāmoans'.

A few weeks earlier, the lunchtime bell had rung and they were standing in front of us, crowding around the exit. They always seemed to travel in packs, when I think about it. But thankfully my best friends, Teuila and Masina, were with me.

Teuila was the coconut-oiled, tanned one. She was every parent and teacher's dream. Then there was Masina, who described herself as 'mahogany brown', because she was all creative and stuff. 'Creativity and art are my forte,' she would say. Whatever that meant.

Teuila and Masina already knew each other from church, and then they found me, the third afakasi musketeer. The light-skinned one, or the 'tinted beige one', Masina would say, as Teuila's good-girl-giggle filled the background.

Masina was so cheeky. But we didn't mind, because we knew we were her outlet from her 'islander prison home' – her words, not mine.

As we walked past the Real Sāmoans, their leader, Vai, stepped into our path, blocking our way out. Vai had come from Sāmoa at the beginning of the year. Her presence alone was intimidating. Even her shadow seemed angry.

Vai started saying something in Sāmoan – a familiar and yet unfamiliar language to me. I smiled politely, thinking *this is a bit awkward*, as they didn't return the smile and were just looking at us, up and down like we'd stepped into landmine territory or something.

Masina, the witty one, was entertaining them with what sounded like islander small talk. This always reminded me of how I wished I could speak and understand Sāmoan. Teuila then turned to me and whispered, 'They've asked what we're eating for lunch.'

'I've got nothing, that's why we're going to the cantee -'

Then Teuila interrupted me, turning to them, spitting out a flurry of words with a smile, giving them the chicken roll she'd bought at the bakery before school. We turned around and walked off as if we knew where we were going. But we didn't – or at least, I didn't.

'The freshies are so hun-gus,' Masina said as we walked the long way behind the school hall to the canteen.

'Hey, they're not freshies, they just know what they know and that's just the islander way – sharing is caring,' said Teuila.

'Well maybe if they cared more we *would* share, plus they need to get with the programme – *hello*, they're in New Zealand now, you can't just go asking people for their lunch,' snapped Masina.

'I would have bought them something', I said

innocently.'

'Then they'd never leave us alone, bloody fobs,' said Masina.

'Ahhh, we're all fobs,' said Teuila sarcastically, followed by her good-girl giggling again to break Masina out of her rant – which it did, as she started laughing too.

I just followed along like I knew what was happening, even though I didn't fully know what a 'fob' was. Plus I was definitely not going to let Masina know that I didn't, I'd never have heard the end of it. But what I did know was that I trusted Masina, and Teuila had my back. And they always did.

It wasn't long before I came across the Real Sāmoans by myself, defenceless and unarmed, without my translators and navigators, Masina and Teuila.

They must have smelled the fear as they turned the corner, slowly heading towards me. The Real Sāmoans terrified me. Not because they were physically the Goliath in this fight, but because they were aware of the war that I had no idea I was in.

Vai was at the front, leading the pack who looked ahead, seeing me approaching. It all happened at double speed, the Sāmoan words flying in the air as I tried to smile and nod my way past. Amused faces turning unimpressed. Shrinking in my shoes, feeling smaller than small, they threw Sāmoan words at me like darts, expecting me to respond when they knew I couldn't. Then, just before the first tear fell, Vai led them away, their loud murmurs and giggles echoing through the school corridors: 'E lē o se teine Sāmoa … o le plastic Sāmoan … pālagi,' they said, making sure I stayed down and knew my place.

They finally turned the corner, giving me time to catch my breath and sit in my own plastic Sāmoan pālagi tears.

I tried to gather myself, to make sense of it all before I got to Miss Smith's class. Feeling not afakasi, not Sāmoan; feeling nothing.

'Just accept it. They're right,' I thought. What did I know about being Sāmoan?

There's a language, and things my dad, aunties and uncles do, that I really don't know anything about. I don't even know what Sāmoa is actually like, because I've never been. Mum refuses to go because the mosquitos supposedly love her pālagi skin. When we were younger, Dad had to go to Sāmoa for his uncle Tino's funeral, and we had to give our clothes and old toys. Then Dad came back complaining how hot it was. So it must be a poor, hot place I guess?

Being a plastic Sāmoan must mean not knowing much about being Sāmoan? If that's the case – yeah, that's me.

And it's obvious what makes me pālagi. My mum. Everything I inherited from her. Like when Katie told me at our Year 9 school camp, 'You don't have islander feet.'

Curious, I asked Katie, 'What are islander feet?'

'It's big wide feet and short stubby toes,' she said, laughing. I wasn't sure whether she was laughing at the fact that I didn't know, or at her description of islander feet.

So yeah they're right – Plastic Sāmoan, yes,

definitely. Pālagi, absolutely.

Interrupting the jury's verdict in my head, I heard Miss Lata's voice. 'Lani, are you okay?' I blinked fast, looking at the ground and said, 'Yip, just heading to Miss Smith's class.'

Miss Lata didn't buy it. Then the bell suddenly went for the next period and Miss Lata said, 'Okay, Lani, it's a busy week with learning conferences after school, so why don't you pop into my class first thing tomorrow morning and we can have a proper catch up?'

Miss Lata was my dean and the head of the History department. I couldn't wait to take History with her as a brand new senior next year. She was the best teacher ever. She got us, most probably because she was Sāmoan herself and was just real with us, but in an islander way.

That's why we regularly caught up with her to check in and vent about school and life.

'Okay, Miss, thanks. I'll see you tomorrow and I'll bring Teuila and Masina too.' I smiled bravely, making my way to my Social Studies class.

I took a seat next to Teuila, who was sitting at our usual window table as Miss Smith wrote on the whiteboard. I couldn't believe it was only Thursday. But I took comfort in the fact that it was the last period of the day.

I felt safe with my islander bodyguard Teuila, who turned to ask if I'd finished the latest Social Studies assignment yet – and then stopped. She knew I'd been crying and automatically put her arm around me.

I saw Vai's reflection in the window, sitting in her

9

usual seat at the back of the class. I looked past her reflection and saw the rest of the Real Sāmoans walking across the courtyard to their classes, waving and smiling goodbye to Vai as they disappeared into another building.

Frustrated and angry, I turned to Teuila and said, 'If they're real Sāmoans, I don't think I ever want to be one.'

Teuila's arm squeezed me for extra comfort as Miss Smith started the roll call for class to begin.

CHAPTER 2

Teuila Ekanesio

I walked into the kitchen to notify Mum: 'Tinā o le faifeau lea ua sau.'

Mum quickly fired off instructions. 'Va'ai po ua vela kalo ma sa'eu le sapasui,' while washing her hands and making her way to the lounge.

Being a teine Sāmoa can be lonely at times, especially when you're the only girl and your brothers are useless. Armed with my 'ie lavalava around my waist, my perfect high bun and welcoming smile, I was the first responder to feau or chores, cooking, babysitting, helping my brothers with their homework; to ushering guests, to siva, to attend to, to help. All with a smile on my face. So when I got bored, I would make it all a game, like I was being judged for a Miss Sāmoa contest with only one contestant.

'This teine Sāmoa job is no joke,' I would say in my professional voice, making my friends Lani and Masina giggle. I could never keep a straight face, and I was the worst actor.

'Teuila,' Mum called from the lounge.

'O a'u lenei tinā,' I said, quickly racing to her side and kneeling.

'Tapena mai se iputī i luma nei,' she said.

I took the orders for two teas – for the faifeau and mum – and one coffee, for dad. I returned balancing a tray on which were the hot drinks on hardly-ever-been-used saucers; a bowl of sugar and a small porcelain jug of milk, accompanied by a small selection of biscuits. As per my training, only the good plates and cutlery for church ministers.

I took my seat at the end of the room near the lounge door, in case my parents or the visitors needed anything. Everything was a sign or symbol of faaaloalo or respect. From my 'ie lavalava tied around my waist, which draped around my legs covering my lower body, to ensuring I used 'tulou', meaning excuse me, when I walked in front of anyone, especially adults or elders. Serving our visitors their refreshments sitting to the side of the coffee table, not in front of them.

Basically doing everything my parents said, to make them happy and proud.

And this makes *me* happy and proud. Everything I do represents my parents and my family in my islander world and the pālagi world outside.

Then, out of the blue, Dad's cell phone rang and he excused himself to answer it in the hallway.

'Tālofa – oi! Oh, hello, John. How are ya mate?' Dad answering the phone in his Sāmoan-English-Kiwi voice made me giggle to myself as I sat in my spot. If my brothers had been here we would have been re-enacting Dad being a 'switcher', as we call it. Something that's a necessity, being a

New Zealand-born teine Sāmoa.

We were all professional switchers, and Mum would say, 'Faamuamua lau gagana Sāmoa i totonu o lou 'āiga auā a ē alu i le ā'oga, ona maua lea o le gagana inilisi.' So basically it was: 'Sāmoan at home, English at school - Teine Sāmoa at home and teine pālagi outside.'

Mum's English is polished, as she's an office manager and it's a requirement to speak good clear English, I guess. Dad, on the other hand, knows phrases well, but the gaps in his English show when he tries to string a sentence together, which is probably why he speaks in short English sentences.

For me, it was the same at school. I spoke perfect English and was a professional chameleon. I knew when and how to be a teine Sāmoa, and I saw how hard my parents worked in our Sāmoan and pālagi world. I needed to do the same. I did everything to make them proud.

Our household was Sāmoan-speaking-only until the outside world came in, and then English was on. English was for school and work. But sometimes these two very different worlds would overlap too.

Mum once told me that when I started school, the pālagi teacher suggested that she speak more English at home, as I was getting confused with the pronunciation of vowels when trying to read English books. Then at intermediate, my teacher told me I needed to participate more in discussions and ask more questions. But questioning was definitely not part of being a teine Sāmoa. We also don't have the freedom to hang out with friends, talk on the phone or worry about our nails. I can still hear my mum saying, 'O le teine Sāmoa e iloa ona o tomai i le fāiga o le āuli, tagamea, kuka ma fe'au uma o le lotoifale.'

Even having friends was frowned upon; they were considered distractions unless they were godly girls from church. Luckily I had Masina, who understood all the teine Sāmoa issues I was going through, Masina being the daughter of our faifeau – our guest that day – and thankfully I also had Lani, who was a junior prefect with me at school, so she passed my parents' high educational standards and expectations. Plus, she was half pālagi so she was destined to win in the pālagi world and could help me, according to my parents.

When Dad returned to his seat, he apologised for the phone call. As the church's treasurer, he joined the discussion of the upcoming car-wash fundraiser for the new choir uniforms.

'Aua le popole,' said the faifeau in response to Dad's apology. Then he acknowledged me by saying, 'Teine lelei tele oe Teuila.'

My parents smiled proudly, telling the faifeau how they always remind me: 'Ia e faamuamua le Atua i lou olaga ma e faafetaia ai pea le Atua ona o le faalogo ma usita'i.

They all nodded in agreement.

I got the signal that the little fono was wrapping up. I'd already prepared the take-home plate of food for the faifeau, left over from Dad's roast lamb last night, as tonight's chop suey still wasn't ready. I also got the feeling that mum wanted it just for us – especially as the boys would be home from rugby training soon and they'd be starving for a big feed.

The faifeau happily took the plate of food, mentioning that he'd most likely see my parents again at our school learning conferences tomorrow, waving farewell as he made his way out.

CHAPTER 3

Masina Fetu

'Faalogo ma usita'i.' The prescription for happiness in my household, aka islander prison. Something I followed religiously all my life, not just because Dad is a faifeau and discipline in our family is based around God seeing everything, but also because I love my parents and it's just what a good teine Sāmoa does.

But when my intermediate teacher told them that I like to draw, and that I should seriously consider continuing Art at high school, my dad's short, sharp response was, 'No thanks.' I remember my teacher's facials. It was like she'd sworn – and she had. This teacher had dropped the D-bomb. Drawing.

It was the first time I realised my dad had something against drawing. I hadn't even known it was a bad thing. Like, hello? It wasn't boys, parties or drugs – it was *drawing*. It was literally the eleventh commandment I never knew about.

I've always loved drawing; how it has let me express myself, especially since open communication wasn't really a big thing for our family and my island prison life.

I felt like drawing was in my blood. 'Another extension or a part of myself, like my sixth sense,' I said to my friend Lani. She just rolled her light brown afakasi eyes. I laughed to myself. I hadn't expected her to get it, since she still drew stick figures.

Honestly, it allowed me to focus and create a place I wished I lived in. One made of new shapes and random objects; one that didn't always have to follow the often suffocating directions that ruled my real life. I was the scribe and creator of the worlds I created, and this gave me the freedom my soul needed to keep going within the complicated restrictions of my existence.

Fast forward two years, to a Thursday evening learning conference, where I found myself sitting next to my parents, across from my Social Studies teacher. The upside was I was in my final conference for the year, and it was my final junior year in high school.

Miss Smith was a slender, brown-haired pālagi woman who clearly loved her job. She was excited as she chatted non-stop about herself and her day as we entered the room, obviously eager to report my progress to my parents.

'Lovely to see you again, Pastor and Mrs Fee-too,' Miss Smith said.

How hard is it to say Fetu? I thought, fake-smiling away.

She continued happily telling my parents, 'So Masina is doing extremely well, works well with others and always finishes her work to a high standard, like her last assignment which she handed in early yesterday, about your family journey.' She proudly showed it to Mum and Dad.

Since Dad had been busy all week organising the church fundraiser, I'd only interviewed Mum, which had made it really quick. My work was meticulous. Answers typed in simple font and it was easy to see that my Journeys assignment for this Social Studies class was perfect. *Winning!* I thought to myself.

I was so busy analysing my parents' satisfied reactions, I almost missed it. 'Masina also demonstrates some amazing drawing skills,' Miss Smith said, pulling out a piece of paper on which was a representation of my parents' journey from Sāmoa to New Zealand. Traditional tatau designs emerging from a fale Sāmoa in the middle.

I held my breath, taken off guard.

'She handed this in with her assignment, and it's just beautiful!' said Mrs Smith, glowing with pride. 'But it would be good for Masina to draw in her own art pad, instead of in her social studies book. But she does show exceptional skill.'

I thought to myself, 'OMG, you and your but … but … Lady – just stop already!'

Dad snapped out of his happy place. 'O le ā le mea lea Masina?'

Miss Smith noticed the sudden language switch and my father's tone, so she quickly added, 'But it's not impacting her work at the moment, and I've talked to Mr Walker, our Art teacher, and he would love to have Masina in their Art extension class. I think it'll be good for Masina to have a place where she can be creative and develop her art skills. Next year she could possibly take it as a senior, he said –

they enter art competitions and even do student exhibitions for the school.'

My father's silence made us all nervous. Even Miss Smith's energy went down a notch. But the look he gave me lit a fuse that would lead to an inevitable explosion, most likely in the car – especially as islanders aren't good at being patient. Making it to the house wasn't going to be an option.

Miss Smith just sat there, waiting for a response. She had no clue about the impact of her words – that what she'd said and what my parents had heard were two different things. Dad had only heard - *Drawing ... not the time or the place ... develop her art skills*. The unspoken eleventh commandment broken again.

I caught my mother's expression out of the corner of my eye. She was a soft soul, a supportive faletua who agreed with Dad that anything besides school work was an unnecessary distraction. That included drawing. She reminded me daily of how strict her life was, growing up as a minister's daughter in Sāmoa and the sacrifices they'd made so that I could have everything they'd never had.

But I knew Mum was heartbroken. She hung her head ever so slightly, which spoke of her mixture of feeling for me, and disappointment, while also bowing her head in submission to Miss Smith in remorse for her disobedient daughter's actions.

Miss Smith tried to get the mood back on track, breaking the silence by asking, 'So, Masina, how do you think you are going with your learning in my class?'

I didn't want to look up. I felt my dad's laser beam

19

eyes burning through the back of my head. I put on my brave face and said, 'Sorry, Miss Smith, about the drawing. I'll make sure it doesn't happen again.' I knew better than to speak my mind; how I really felt like saying, 'Dad – you totally missed that I'm doing amazing at everything,' or, 'Miss Smith, your work is way too easy and I only draw in my book when I've finished all your boring work anyway ... plus you said it's not even impacting my work at the moment, so the problem is?' Or that it just didn't matter what I said. Because the world and everyone in it had made up their minds: I wasn't following their rules, so I was wrong.

My father followed my apology with a stern one of his own, indicating the seriousness of the matter. And Miss Smith tried to retract her words by emphasising more examples of all the great things I'd done.

You and your 'buts', lady, need to just ... to just butt out. Too little, too late.

We left the meeting, and the tension got worse as we walked towards the car. Mum and Dad walked ahead, as if not wanting to be associated with me. The way they slammed the car doors made me wonder if they were going to just drive off and leave me for good.

As I reached for the car door handle I was somewhat disappointed that they hadn't.

The list of consequences for my love of drawing came hard and fast. 'Masina, 'faalogo mai ... What did we say about drawing? ... No more TV.' Followed by the impact on my future as a lawyer – something they had decided on long before I could walk. 'Drawing won't get you into university … You're wasting time, and where will drawing get you? How will you get into law school?'

The comparisons to others, justifying their disappointment. 'Look at Teuila, e faalogo ma usita'i i ona mātua … She's clever because she listens and loves her parents.'

Then the personal attack on my parents and our people. 'Everything we have done for you, and this is what you do at school … We didn't come to New Zealand for you to draw … the pālagi teacher must think we're all valea.'

I took it all, because I knew what would happen if I were to answer these rhetorical questions. It was like baiting me to answer. And then the consequences would be justified due to me not listening and being disrespectful – faalogo ma usita'i. Part of my parents' job was helping me learn that the choices I made were wrong, and not to do it again. It was discipline, learning and love. All combined.

Then Dad would ask, 'E i ai sou gutu?' The only response I could give was, 'Sorry,' to show I had realised my wrongdoing, instead of letting him know what I really wanted to say: 'One day I'll give you my mouth ... I'm going to join the Art extension class … because I deserve it and have done everything you've asked of me! What is your problem with drawing anyway?'

He must have read my mind. His last words on the matter were, 'Taofi le tusiga o na ata. Aua ne'i o'u toe va'ai o tusi na ata. E te iloa le mea e te o'o i ai … Masina – no more drawing.'

As my mother chimed in with her, 'Masina ia e toaga

21

e tatalo …' I tuned out and quietly wept in the back of the car, wishing I had my pad and pen to draw a new world. Or better yet, to erase me altogether from this one.

CHAPTER 4

Vai Amosa

The beginning of the year

Moping around the room, slowly packing her final trinkets, favourite ili and sei, Vai paused. 'Ou te lē fia alu in Niu Sila tinā,' she said boldly.

'Usitaʻi i laʻu upu ma tapena lau ato,' snapped her mother as she swung her arm back and forth with the salu, doing a final clean of her bedroom.

Quickly wiping her tears away, Vai managed to say, 'O loʻu atunuʻu moni Sāmoa,' finally getting her mother's attention.

Taking pity on her daughter, she walked over, saying in a comforting voice, 'Sauni tatou uō i Niu Sila e maua ai le lumanaʻi i āʻoga ma galuega ma fesoasoani mai i le tatou ʻāiga i Sāmoa.'

It was no use – she was going whether she liked it or not. And it was definitely a not.

Who was going to feed Sefo, the unkempt orangey-brown chicken; who would fofō grandma's legs in the morning? And who would be the narrator for lotu tamaiti this year? *I've just won the speech contest. What use will speaking Sāmoan be in New Zealand?*

Her angry thoughts were interrupted by her mother. 'Teine lelei, alu e sauni le to'ona'i.'

Her mother, Sosefina, was from the village of Vailoa and had run away to be with Vai's father, Mikaele. They lived in her father's family house in the village of Fusi, with Nana Ana and Papa Pati. Her father's twin sister, Aunty Sia, her husband Uncle Ioane and their two kids Masi and Tali were their closest family members, and they had come for their final farewell to'ona'i. Tali was also her best friend. They had grown up together and were just a year apart. She was the closest thing Vai had to a sister, and she was going to be leaving her behind.

Tali was her final thought before defeat took over and carried her to the kitchen, where Nana was fussing with the taro. Vai started collecting the plates from the shelf, gently placing them on the table. Her nana squeezed her shoulders and sent her a sad mix of love and heartbreak through her kind, wise eyes.

Masi was playing with his toy car in the lounge, stopping every now and then to check what food was being placed on the table. Aunty Sia had just finished, and was saying her farewells to Dad. She put on a brave smile just for Vai as she emerged from the back door, wiping her tears away with her 'ie lavalava.

'Ua e sauni ete alu i Niu Sila? Talofae e, ese lou teine lelei,' Aunty Sia said, giving Vai a sympathy hug.

If everyone's so sad, this is obviously not a good idea. Why can't everyone see this?

Out of the corner of her eye, Vai saw Tali coming up

the driveway with the basket of umu goodies from Seti, their neighbour. Nana was now calling out to Papa Pati to take his seat at the head of the table. Vai quickly finished setting up the table and ran outside to meet Tali.

The grey cloud over Tali's head joined Vai's as they embraced. Vai then helped Tali carry one side of the basket.

'O le ā le umi e te alu ai Niu Sila?' asked Tali.

'Ou te leiloa' replied Vai.

This made the mood worse.

'Amuia oe o le a e alu i Niu Sila', said Tali.

'E sili lava lo'u 'āiga ma ā'oga i Sāmoa ia te a'u,' replied Vai, with deep sadness in her voice.

Walking into the kitchen, Nana Ana, Papa Pati, Mum, Aunty Sia and Uncle Ioane were all seated at the table. Masi was grinning at Tali and Vai because he'd squeezed on to his mother's knee, which meant he'd now be able to eat first, with the adults. Tali gave him an evil look as he sneakily poked his tongue out at her.

Vai and Tali prepared to serve their to'ona'i for their family for the final time together. Sua i'a in cups. Check. Placing the luau and ulu from the umu on the table. Check. The final touches for their farewell feast. Check.

The adults started talking about the recent village news of Vili's shop down the road being bought out by the Chinese, who they believed were planning to take over Sāmoa. Everyone tuned in while they waited for Dad to join them. He was outside finishing the fence he'd promised to build Papa Pati before they left.

As the topic turned to Mum's cousin Lui, who'd

married a pālagi in New Zealand and had supposedly forgotten how to be a tama Sāmoa, having turned into a pālagi himself, Tali went to check on Dad to give him the final call for to'ona'i.

Vai stopped for a minute and took in everything. The sights – the brightly coloured furniture, pictures of 'āiga, her family together. The sounds – Sefo the chicken clucking about the yard; the laughter; Nana teasing Papa for being faipē. Just the feeling of home.

Dad walked into the room in a happy mood. He was excited, Vai could tell.

'E sili lava Niu Sila e tele faamanuiaga e maua ai,' Vai had heard him say to Mum just before Christmas last year.

'Niu Sila?' Vai thought to herself. Not knowing that she would be leaving so soon.

Finally, Mikaele took his seat opposite Papa Pati. This was the unspoken indicator for the farewell proceedings to start. The table quieted as Papa Pati put on a stoic voice and spoke on behalf of the family. They'd been dreading this moment, when their emotions would be put on the table.

Tears silently fell from their faces. Apart from Masi's, as he, of course, was still focused on getting to the moa and his favourite sapasui and oka before anyone else.

Vai started to sob loudly and was pulled into Nana Ana's embrace. 'Aua e te tagi loto tele,' she whispered.

Mikaele cleared his throat, wanting to respond as stoically as his father. He acknowledged everything Nana and Papa had done for him and his family, and he vowed to carry out God's plan for him to serve and support the family.

The jokester of the family, Mikaele ended on a light note to break the tension as their tears started drying, mentioning how excited he was to go on an aeroplane, producing his ticket and showing off his name: Mikaele Amosa. It would be the first time their entire family had been on a plane.

As everyone laughed, Vai, feeling defeated, thought, *It had better be worth it*.

CHAPTER 5

Petelo Sio & Sarah Sio

I sat in the lounge, acting like I couldn't hear anything.

'Not again,' said Mum. I'd heard that tone before. 'I'm sick of giving money, Petelo.'

Dad looked angry as Mum walked off towards their bedroom, clearly not happy.

'What's the big deal, Sarah?' he said, following her. 'We have it ... I hardly see my family because I work so much, and I've told you before, it's about alofa and 'āiga, they need our help. It's what we do.' Dad lowered his voice mid-sentence, as if he'd suddenly remembered I could hear, and Sofia was in her bedroom next door, probably Facebook stalking.

'It's not what *we* do, it's what your family do,' said Mum. It sounded like she wasn't going to budge this time.

'Hey – remember, my family is your family. You married me knowing I was Sāmoan,' Dad said angrily.

Now you did it, Dad, I thought to myself.

Mum hated the obvious being pointed out. That she was bright white and pālagi as it comes, and stood out in our 'tinted beige' family. I guess that's why she stuck to what she knew and ran our family home the pālagi way, while Dad worked and then was too tired to be islander.

Dad would tell us we were Sāmoan, but we never did anything Sāmoan. He worked as a team leader at an accounting firm. He would say to his islander friends that at work, he was the chocolate chip. But I didn't get it, because all I knew about was the pālagi parts of the cookie.

I mean, I'd ask questions, but he often wouldn't answer, because he was busy. And Mum would just refer me back to Dad. I got the idea of what Sāmoans looked like from Dad's friends and his family – medium-to-dark complexion, usually medium-to-large sized and, depending on Mum's mood, she'd joke that Sāmoans don't have very much, go to church, and ask for heaps of money.

My sister Sofia was blessed with thick skin and a big mouth. So she'd be the one to give Mum a go, saying, 'There are plenty of pālagi people who don't have very much, go to church and ask for money actually, mother dearest.'

I wished I was as brave as Sofia, then maybe Vai and her gang wouldn't have got to me at school today.

We would see our Sāmoan family only on important occasions, like birthdays, and even then Mum always acted like a guest, like she wasn't used to the surroundings or thought they weren't up to her standard.

But I loved it. Our Sāmoan family is larger than life, with all the aunties trying to sneak us treats, kidnap us sometimes because we were 'so cute' and always trying to shower us with love and food! Oh, the food!

I really wish we saw them more.

'I married you, Petelo, not your culture,' said Mum.

Dad was silent, which was strange. Maybe Mum had

won?

Sofia came into the lounge, interrupting my eavesdropping, and plonked herself on the leather lazy boy next to me.

I whispered, 'What's all that about?' looking in the direction of Mum and Dad's room.

Sofia is four years older than me, and she knows a whole lot more, including about Sāmoan stuff, because she was brought up with Dad's family when she was younger. She was born around the time that Dad had decided to make a career change and was finishing his uni studies, and Mum had to go back to work to support them. So Dad's family stepped in to help raise Sofia. They even gave her a Sāmoan nickname, Sala, which Mum wasn't very fond of and never used.

I just wished I'd had that time with them too, because she knew so much more about being Sāmoan and the whole islander world.

'Another faalavelave,' Sofia said.

'What's that?' I replied, puzzled.

'Remember, it's when there's like a wedding or a funeral, or an event that the whole family contributes money towards to help out or show support and stuff,' said Sofia as she switched the TV channel, smiling when she saw her favourite commercial was on.

It was everyone's favourite commercial, actually. The Cadbury chocolate one where this big hairy gorilla plays the drums. I don't know what it had to do with chocolate, but as random as it was, it was definitely working, judging by how Sofia was buying chocolate with any spare cash she got. Luckily, she usually shared.

'Why doesn't Mum want to help?' I whispered, in case Mum and Dad emerged from their bedroom.

'It's not that she doesn't want to,' said Sofia, her eyes still glued to the TV. 'She just doesn't get it. She's pālagi and she tries to be polite, but she doesn't understand Sāmoan ways. That's what I heard Aunt Lupe say, anyway.' Aunty Lupe was Dad's sister, and she was always teasing Dad about being pālagi himself.

'Is that why Mum doesn't want us speaking Sāmoan?' I asked curiously.

'Yeah, because she doesn't get it. She once said to me it won't be any use to us when we need to speak English for school and work anyway.' Sofia's tone was nonchalant.

That's not fair, I thought.

Dad appeared in the lounge doorway and asked, 'Girls, do you want anything from the shops? I've got to get some money out.'

'Yeah – some Cadbury chocolate please, Dad,' said Sofia.

I looked at him with sorry eyes and shook my head.

As he left, I whispered to Sofia, 'Man, I thought Mum had won.'

Sofia, slowly rocking to the gorilla's drumming, replied, 'Nope. Dad told her that his culture is part of him, not separate.'

This brought a smile to my face.

'Where's this song from, Sofia?' I asked, watching Dad's car reverse out of our driveway.

'It's by this old dude called Philip or something, I think – is that right, Mum?' Sofia called. Mum was now stomping around in the kitchen.

'What, Sofia?' she muttered.

'On the TV – who sings this song?'

Mum popped her head into the lounge and said, 'Phil Collins. It's called "In the Air Tonight".' Then she went back to stomping around in the kitchen.

The Sāmoan spirit in me wanted more, and I decided to wait for Dad to return to let him know, because if it was part of him, it must definitely be part of me, right? I think about that as the commercial slowly comes to an end … *I can feel it coming in the air tonight, oh Lord* …

CHAPTER 6

Filipo Fetu & Ruta Fetu

Filipo's old knees were about to give way, so he lifted himself up from kneeling on the lounge floor, carefully turning his body to sit on the armchair he'd been leaning on for his evening prayers. Tonight they were delayed due to Masina's learning conference.

His eye was caught by the colourful ula hanging from the cherished photos and diplomas adorning the lounge walls. A certificate of completion from the prestigious Sāmoa College. His graduation certificate from Malua Theology College. Top of the class. He smiled to himself as he scanned the surrounding pictures of home, enjoying the warm memories they brought. Then he stopped at the picture of his family all gathered under their faleoʻo.

It took him back to watching the dogs patrol their boundary where a fence should have been; instead it was marked out by a tree trunk and a line of trees carrying their daily nourishment – ulu, avocado, laichee. It was a beautiful sight. His favourite thing to watch from the faleo'o was the frangipanis glistening in the sunlight, swaying with the warm breeze, helping him to pass the time as he sat day after day in the faleo'o, by his father's side as his number one assistant and apprentice as an ʻau koso.

His father was the great tufuga ta tatau, master tattooist, Seupule Fetu. The family's faleo'o was his father's headquarters and was the only place Filipo could spend time with his father. He was always busy with tatau – pe'a and malu, creating new designs and even sleeping amongst his pictures. It was a family tradition passed down from Filipo's great grandfather to his grandfather and now his father.

Filipo's grandfather was revered across Sāmoa, and highly sought after for his special techniques and attention to detail. Filipo's own father was believed to be a living and breathing tatau, due to his extensive knowledge of cultural symbols – where they originated from and the stories behind them. This was why he was always in demand. From everybody. Leaving his only son Filipo with the scraps of time he had left over.

His father constantly talked about tatau. 'It's a gift from God, and a part of our spirit is in every tatau … you become the essence of the tatau,' he would say.

Filipo watched as the years passed by and his father dedicated more time and his life to tatau. Filipo grew worried for his father, taking over from his dad sometimes, because he feared it would kill him in the end.

As the son of Sāmoa's very own tatau master, Filipo was automatically made his understudy to carry the family tradition and his father's legacy into the future. It was a role he never really wished for, because he knew that God had bigger plans for him.

His mother Ruta's family had their own family tradition. She was the only daughter of the village faifeau,

Tino Va'a. Tino disapproved of his daughter's union with Seupule, probably because he was the exact opposite to Seupule – he gave Filipo guidance; he was caring, gave him time, taught him about the love of God and basically became the father figure Filipo had longed for all his life.

Grandpa Tino also emphasised the importance of school and how Filipo could be the one to carry on the family tradition of being a faifeau. He knew Filipo was clever and capable. Book smart. He was a natural at school – something his father didn't really value, having never finished school himself because his destiny was already set. This was why he urged Filipo to finish up school, to fulfil his own tufuga destiny.

Mr Tupola, the school principal, had told Filipo he could be anything he wanted to when he grew up. But Filipo would smile politely, knowing that in fact he couldn't. Plus, if he was really honest, he just wanted to be free of his tufuga fate, for which he had a growing resentment.

Then one day, Grandpa Tino told him about a scholarship being offered to Malua Theology College. Filipo took this as a sign his prayers had been answered. He began to believe that if he became a faifeau, he wouldn't be allowed to be a tufuga, and that maybe he'd be sent away, hopefully overseas, to escape the guilt he'd feel towards his father, and that one day in the future he'd be able to give his own family the life he dreamed of. One where they wouldn't have to be dependent on the land for survival, where the importance of education was valued, where *he* would be valued.

This was going to be his ticket out from his destined life as the next tufuga master.

Later that week Filipo thought it would be a good time to tell his father. A matai had travelled from New Zealand to get his tatau done, so Dad had received a generous payment and gifts, even though he gave some of it back. He was in a good mood, which was all Filipo needed. As his father checked over his cleaning of the 'au ta, Filipo took a deep breath and told him that he was applying for the scholarship to Malua theology college. His father didn't even flinch as he inspected the tools, as if nothing had been said.

Then, just before we went inside, he turned to Filipo and said, 'E le mafai ona e tufuga ma e faifeau i le taimi e tasi.'

Filipo nodded his head, too scared to speak in case the disappointment in the air changed his mind.

His father turned away, walked inside, and Filipo watched as he turned the house lights off, leaving him by himself in the dark, a place he was used to.

A few weeks later, the day came when Filipo would assist his father with a tatau for the last time. He'd won the scholarship and been accepted into Malua Theology College, and was going to live with Grandpa Tino in preparation.

A female taupou from Saoluafata lay before them; her name was Masina. She was the strongest and bravest person he'd ever seen undergo a tatau. Her malu was inspired by the legend of Nafanua, the great Sāmoan goddess and warrior. She hardly flinched throughout the entire process, almost smiling as the tatau teeth broke her skin over and over again, asking to extend each session, tiring his father. Masina said the pain made her feel stronger, and she could feel the spirit of Nafanua entering her body as the ink found a new home under her skin.

This was how Filipo felt. The pain he'd caused felt necessary, and in many ways was so freeing. But his father didn't see it like that – he hadn't spoken to him since Filipo had broken the news.

Masina's malu was one of his father's best works, and for the first time ever, Filipo saw his father shed tears as the final ceremony with the beautiful Masina ended. Supporters believed the tears were due to the malu glowing in the sunset as they celebrated its completion, but Filipo knew. He understood his father knew it was over. A tradition, a history, a legacy. But what neither knew was that this would be the last time they would see each other.

Filipo refused to believe that his leaving had killed his father. He had even predicted that the tufuga life would be the death of him.

This is why Filipo named his only daughter Masina. She was a symbol of hope in the dark, an homage to his father and a farewell to the pain of the past. She represented the strength needed to move into the new future he'd carved out of his dreams – for him, his family and their future – something Masina held in the palm of her hands. Whether she knew it or not.

From the sounds of Masina's tears down the hallway, Filipo knew she didn't know. She didn't know any of it, and that wasn't her fault. He realised that now, he was trying to control her destiny.

Filipo quietly wept to himself, as did Masina in her bedroom. God had finally answered his prayer.

CHAPTER 7

Mele Ekanesio & Setefano Ekanesio

To: teuila@phs.school.nz

From: E.Smith@phs.school.nz

Subject: Social Studies – Journeys Assignment

- Assignment Task 1: Create questions to complete an interview with your parent(s)/caregiver about their personal journey to or within NZ.

- Assignment Task 2: Compare the answers from your interview in Task 1 with your own journey so far and complete a personal journey reflection.

Assignment Task 1: The Interview

Interviewee Names: Mele Ekenasio (Mum) and Setefano Ekenasio (Dad)

1. O fea sa e fanau ai?
   Mele: Sa 'ou fanau i le falema'i i Moto'otua i Sāmoa – Teuila, fai fesili pālagi because it's for school. I was born in Moto'otua Hospital in Sāmoa.
   Setefano: E tutusa la ma lo'u tinā.

Mele: Setefano – fai faaigilisi.

Setefano: Oi! Sorry – same as your mother.

2.   Where do you come from in Sāmoa?

Mele: My mother's village is Afega and my father's village is Vaisala.

Setefano: My father came from Falelatai and my mother came from Aleisa, right at the top of ...

Mele: Faapu'upu'u lau tala!

3.   What was life like in Sāmoa?

Mele: Village life was very simple. We had to help our parents a lot with chores and our younger siblings. Dad was the only one who worked – as a bus driver – to support all six of us. So school was very important. To get a good education and do well, get a good job to help Mum and Dad.

Setefano: Hard. Get up early. Help Grandad at plantation. Grandma look after us. We didn't have heaps of food. But we happy ... we didn't care. We play with cousins and ate food we grow at home.

4.   What was school like?

Mele: I loved it. I got into Sāmoa College and I was the first one in my family. I did well and then I came to New Zealand to work.

Setefano: Good at school but was hard learning English. We not allowed to speak Sāmoan.

Me: Aiseā tamā? Why was that, Dad?

Setefano: Don't know. It was how it was. I get detentions for speaking Sāmoan and always forget to speak English. Pālagi important so English important.

Mele: English was important, Teuila. Everything at school was in English, so you could prepare for your pālagi job. Grandma used to always tell me that Sāmoans who spoke English were better Sāmoans and pālagi liked them better.

Me: Wait, so if you didn't speak English, you weren't important?

Setefano: No, just like no schooling … ahhh o le ā le upu? [scratching his head] … uneducated. Like how the lighter Sāmoans … with light skin Sāmoans were treated better.

Me: Why were light-skin Sāmoans treated better?

Mele: I guess they looked closer to being pālagi I suppose, usually afakasi and good families looked pālagi and were well known in Sāmoa.

Setefano: They are rich too, not like us dark tagata Sāmoa [Dad giggles].

Mele: Teuila don't include this, your faiā'oga will think tagata Sāmoa are valea.

Me: Okay then …

5.   When and why did you come to New Zealand from Sāmoa?

Mele: 1973 – I had finished Sāmoa College and your Aunty Fualole was already living in New Zealand. So we decided it was best for me to live with Aunty and send money back to Grandma and Grandpa to help them.

Setefano: 1976 – Same with Mum. Work. Send money home.

6. What did you think coming to New Zealand was going to be like before you came?

Mele: I was a bit scared and knew I was going to miss my parents. I had never lived anywhere but home. But I was happy I was going to live with Aunty Fualole, she would help me, I thought.

Setefano: I was excited. I thought I was going to be free from my feau. Pay my parents back and make them rich! [Everyone breaks out in hysterical laughter].

7. What was New Zealand actually like?

Mele: It was good. I got a job straight away as an office assistant because I had done so good at school – see Teuila? [Nudges Teuila gently] And I spoke really good English. It helped Grandma and Grandpa rebuild our family home. I was really proud to be able to give back to our family [Eyes start to water].

Setefano: I don't like it at first. Was too different. Fast cars and just busy, always busy. It wasn't nice because my English wasn't good and I was like how they call us – a fob like off the boat. I was lucky, some of my friends were beat up and got the racism. But that's because they weren't fitting in … and some were stand out, like your brother, eh, Mele?

Mele: O Iosefa? Yes, that's right ... your Uncle Iosefa was part of the group who helped new people from the Pacific if they weren't treated right, o le Polynesian Panthers. But we just told him to stop causing trouble for the rest of us.

Me: So wait, you wanted to just fit in, which was being pālagi, speaking English and didn't want to stand out by being Sāmoan? Being yourself?

Setefano: Toe fai mai ua vave lau tautala …

Mele: Teuila va'ai lou gutu – It was what it was. New Zealand was very different to Sāmoa. We couldn't speak Sāmoan to everyone. We had to learn when to be pālagi and when to be Sāmoan.

Setefano: [Nodding] That's how we live. Get through it all.

Me: But that's still how you … we all still cope today, though – how has it changed? Wait – so when and where are you Sāmoan, then?

Mele: What kind of question is that, Teuila? We are always Sāmoan.

Setefano: Teuila fai faalelei lau fesili.

Me: Why did you teach us the Sāmoan language and culture if it's not going to help us in New Zealand?

Mele: Tu'utu'u i lalo lou leo, all this questioning they're teaching you at school is making you a fiapoto.

Me: Do you think we can actually be Sāmoan in the Pālagi world?

Setefano: Toe pau lea o la'u upu ia te oe!

Me: Aua le popole, ua lelei tinā ma tamā. Faafetai tele lava [Leaves the kitchen table].

Assignment task 2: Personal Journey Summary
My initial draft – what I want to submit:
My journey …

Born Teuila Selina Ekenasio, I am a proud teine Sāmoa. But I can only be this in my house and in church. This is because my Sāmoan parents were raised to believe the pālagi world outside is better. It is the best and only way to succeed in New Zealand. So much so that we speak and value English and we deny who we are just to fit in, which means losing or forgetting who we are. I don't see pālagi people changing for us. So I'm screwed unless I break the cycle and be who I am in the pālagi world, but that will mean the pālagi world will treat me as an outsider, a weirdo even … or maybe they can learn about us, understand us and accept us as we are? Then maybe pālagi people can say my name properly for once. And maybe we can be our real selves instead of acting and pretending all the time.

Assignment task 2: Personal Journey Summary
My actual submission:

My journey …

Born Teuila Selina Ekenasio. I am a proud teine Sāmoa. My parents Mele and Setefano came from Sāmoa in the hope of a better life for themselves and their family. The only way they knew how was through ensuring their children had every opportunity to succeed in their education. My parents were brought up with education as a high priority. They are a product of their environment and had to make some sacrifices leaving their homes in Sāmoa. This is why doing good at school is part of my journey and is so important to me, because it is important to them and they have sacrificed a lot for this to happen. I want to share and show who I am, a teine Sāmoa with the world and I also want to be accepted for who I am.

CHAPTER 8

Sosefina Amosa & Mikaele Amosa

'Sau e piki i luga le lapisi lale e tu'u mai o,' Sosefina called out to Vai.

Vai made her way across the classroom, holding the black rubbish bag, narrowly avoiding the neatly stacked row of chairs her mother had just completed. She picked up the rubbish from under the table that 'those fia pālagi' were sitting at hours earlier in her Social Studies class. She hated that class – *a waste of time*, she thought to herself, as Miss Smith just talked so fast and then talked and talked again.

Vai had been helping her mother clean at her school for a few months now, since her dad had got some random work with their Uncle Liko, as a labourer for a construction company that was building new housing developments.

Since moving to New Zealand, life had been new, different, fun, interesting, boring and sad, like a song on repeat.

New and different because New Zealand worked differently, their rules were different, people dressed differently, the weather kept changing throughout the day and it was like they had no time to get used to it because New Zealand was fast – no such thing as island time at all.

Fun and interesting because Vai had started school and found new friends straight away, like Lusia and other girls who had recently come to New Zealand, so they were able to share their stories and laugh at their experiences. They had also joined their Uncle Liko's church, and even though it was a little relaxed compared to back in Sāmoa, it was really nice to have something that felt a little bit like home again.

Sosefina and Mikaele had found jobs straight away, and at first it was great because they'd never had money like this before. But they'd never had bills like this before, either. Paying for a house, a car, furniture, school uniform, food. It all had to come from somewhere. So the dream of sending money home hadn't become a reality yet.

School was very boring, though, and Vai was growing to hate it. She hardly knew what the teachers were talking about, and they often didn't have the patience to try and understand what Vai was talking about, either. She had to rely on her friends to translate most of it.

Vai's culture and language had no use here. She missed Tali, and often thought about her leading the pese at school or even playing volipolo at lunchtime. She couldn't even call her – Mum said it cost too much to call Sāmoa.

The sad part came when Sosefina and Mikaele weren't needed at their factory jobs anymore. They hadn't realised that 'temp' stood for temporary, until the end date arrived.

But Vai thought her dad must have been secretly happy, not having to go back to that job – he said they didn't like islanders, because some of the pālagi he worked with made fun of their English and would laugh if they didn't understand what to do.

They weren't needed anymore, so they 'just chucked us away', Sosefina said. Luckily, Vai's school had been looking for cleaners, and she couldn't be mad at Mum and Dad for taking on cleaning jobs, because they needed to pay the bills somehow. Plus, it was perfect for them because they didn't have to talk to anyone, or have to be around others, acting like they understood them. Thankfully, every now and then Uncle Liko asked Dad to help as a labourer, which was why Vai stepped in to help her Mum.

As Vai wiped down the rest of the student tables, she was reminded of how it felt to not be invited or part of the groups who sat here and how she would pray that her friend Lusia turned up every day just to sit next to her. To not be alone. To just be heard and understood. To be accepted by someone. Especially since Miss Smith and the fia pālagi Sāmoans got to automatically fit in, reminding her that she didn't.

Angrily, Vai reached down to pick up another scrunched-up paper. She opened it – it was the invitation to the learning conferences tomorrow. An invite Vai had purposely not given to her mother, who could barely read these things anyway. Vai would rather be with her mum, making sure her family could put food on the table, than going to hear her teachers tell her how behind she was.

She looked at her mother and ripped up the invitation, placing the scraps in her black rubbish bag, doing

48

a quick scan of the room to see if she'd missed any other rubbish.

'Tatou uō e tapena le isi potu ā'oga,' Sosefina called out to Vai once again.

'Ioe tinā,' she replied, following her mother out, closing the classroom door behind her.

CHAPTER 9

Social Studies Class

Masina quickly sneaked in, joining Teuila and Lani at their window bench just before Miss Smith finished her roll.

Teuila was busy comforting Lani, and nearly missed her name. 'Teuila … Miss E-car-naz-e-oh – hello, are you here?' Teuila's eyes did an imaginary roll into the back of her head as Miss Smith butchered her family name once again. 'Yes, Miss Smith. Sorry, I'm here.'

The teacher continued, 'So, Masina – oh no, there you are. Looks like only Lusia's away today.' She sent off her electronic roll at the push of a button.

'What's wrong with the afakasi queen?' Masina whispered to Teuila, who gave her a *don't-ask-now-and-definitely-not-the-time-to-be-cheeky* look, as Masina quickly reached down for her bag, taking out her book and pencil case.

As Miss Smith explained the set tasks on the board, Lani took out her work, and Teuila breathed a sigh of relief that her friend was okay – or at least okay enough to register what was happening in class.

Lani turned to place her bag under the bench beside her, and saw Vai from the corner of her eye. She was sitting alone, and looking less high and mighty without her crew.

'She *should* be alone, for how she made me feel,' Lani thought to herself. The idea of strength in numbers comforted her.

The class was well underway before Miss Smith did her rounds. 'Masina, have you completed the tasks on the board already?' she said.

'Yes, Miss, this is why I'm drawing, just waiting for the answers to mark, as you said.'

'Okay,' replied Miss Smith. 'Well – maybe no drawing in your actual social studies book.' Then she moved on to Teuila, sitting next to her. 'Very nice, Teuila.'

Before the teacher left their table, Teuila, with a burst of courage, said, 'Excuse me, Miss, will we learn about anything from the Pacific Islands before the end of the year?'

Miss Smith looked puzzled. 'That's a really good question, Teuila. Do you want to learn more about your Tongan history?'

Teuila's eyes nearly popped out of her head as her heart sank, not wanting to correct her teacher. The person who supposedly held her future in her hands didn't even know what she was.

'Yeah, something like that,' she replied.

'The Journeys assignment I emailed at the beginning of the week should cover some personal and cultural history for you,' Miss Smith said with great satisfaction.

'But we won't learn anything about the Pacific Islands or any of its history, in class, then?' said Teuila.

'Well, maybe for one of our school cultural weeks I can ask to include something about Pacific history, or maybe you and Masina could put something together, since you'd be awesome to lead it?' said Miss Smith.

Unable to help herself, Masina said, 'I actually don't know much about Pacific history, only my Cook Island ancestry. So do you know when the cultural week will be, so I can prepare?'

Teuila knew Masina was being her cheeky self, especially since she was not even Cook Islander.

But Masina had saved Teuila from the comment she was fighting to keep in her mouth: *Oh my gosh, thanks so much for letting me be islander for a week*!

'We will sort something, girls,' said Miss Smith. 'Let me have a chat with Miss Lata to see what we can do by the end of the year.'

Teuila had tuned out by then, half-smiling at Miss Smith, hoping she would go away now. Thankfully the rowdy boys across the room caught Miss Smith's attention and she began walking over to them.

'Why is the pālagi way the best way?' said Teuila.

'What do you mean?' said Masina.

'If you want to succeed in this world there's only their way,' replied Teuila. 'Their stuff. Their views. Their history. All of it is more important than our own. It's like they want us to be like them. Even our own islander parents want us to be like them.'

'Because they don't know, Teuila,' said Masina, 'plus they own the world we live in so it's easier to do what they know … which is kind of the same for our parents, doing what they know and just making sure we are doctors and lawyers, not artists.' She let out a sarcastic giggle and shook her head.

'Lani, you're the pālagi here. What do you reckon?' said Masina.

Teuila elbowed Masina, reminding her that Lani might not be ready for her jokes yet. Then Lani suddenly replied, 'I reckon you're right. Some of us pālagi just don't get it, but not because we don't want to, it's just been this way for so long so we don't know any better, sometimes, I guess … But it's not just us pālagi.' She turned to look at Vai. 'It's islanders too – they don't let us in, so I don't know …' She huffed, looking at Teuila, noticing how unusually quiet she was.

'Maybe it's just the way it has to be,' said Masina, scribbling away at the mini islander patterns that now bordered her page.

Hoping to pay back the favour and comfort Teuila, Lani nudged her shoulder and said, 'Maybe Miss Lata can help – she said for us to see her tomorrow morning to catch up. What do you reckon, Teuila?'

Teuila turned to Lani like a lightbulb had gone off. 'I've got it! Yeah, let's see Miss Lata and …'

Miss Smith interrupted their conversation with an announcement to the class. 'Before the bell goes I wanted to remind you about your Journey assignment tasks I sent out on Monday. Thank you to those people who have already handed theirs in – Johnny, Masina and Kahu. The rest of you, don't forget it's due next week, and don't forget to let your parents know that I would love to see them today or tonight after school, even if they haven't made an appointment for their learning conference—'

The bell went.

Like a mini stampede, the class packed up their work and headed for the door, knowing they were free to head home now. Lani's pulse picked up as she packed her stuff up quickly, realising she had to get to basketball training in the gym before her scheduled parent-teacher conference after school.

'See ya in the morning in Miss Lata's class, okay?' she called as she rushed out the door, her mood lifting now the day was over and she was able to get out of the same space as Vai.

Masina remained seated, finishing off her mini art creations in her book, as Teuila got up, tapping her, saying, 'Suga, tatou toe fetaui taeao i le vasega a Miss Lata.' Masina nodded while hypnotised by her now-completed design.

Vai, usually the last one to leave, was walking towards the door at the same time as Teuila. They both stopped as they unexpectedly met at the door. Teuila went to walk through first, and then stopped, took a chance and turned to Vai with an invitation.

CHAPTER 10

Miss Lata

Miss Lata was an island breath of fresh air. She always proudly wore a sei, greeted us with Tālofa and was almost like an aunty to us – the one you get advice from, the one who gives you the truth and tells it to you straight. Most importantly, we trusted her so much that we could be ourselves.

'Malo girls, ua a mai? How are you?' She greeted us with a half hug, an arm round each of us, welcoming us into her class to take a seat. It was a windy Wellington morning, so she'd prepared some koko and offered us all a cup to warm us up.

As we settled in she got straight to the point and asked, 'So how's everyone's week been?'

We looked at each other, wondering who wanted to go first. Teuila dived in, asking, 'Miss – why do you think islanders act pālagi or bow down to pālagi ways, or just to pālagi people in general?'

This took Miss Lata back. 'Alrighty then … where has this come from and what do you mean, Teuila?' she asked.

Without taking a breath, Teuila spat out, 'Well I've been thinking lately, Miss, and honestly I'm just sick of living almost a double life. Like, I love being islander, but we can't be fully islander here at school; we have to be pālagi and the pālagi teachers don't get it, they say our names wrong and think us islanders are all the same. Then even our parents expect us to be full-on islander at home and then do whatever the pālagi says to do to be like them.'

Teuila needed to get it out before she really thought about it, not wanting to give a watered-down edited version, like in her Social Studies Journeys assignment.

'Okay, anything else?' said Miss Lata, as her mind tried to process everything she'd just heard.

Masina chimed in. 'Yeah, I agree, Miss. My parents don't see anything outside of me succeeding like a pālagi, especially through Art. Don't they know pālagi people draw too and it doesn't mean I'm going to end up on the dole or working at the supermarket? And hell yes, pālagi teachers don't get it – oh my gosh did you know Miss Smith told my parents I draw too much in my book even though I achieve excellence in her easy class all year, so it's not even affecting my school work – she just doesn't like having messy books. Seriously, Miss, I can't stand her class now … can you get me taken out?'

Then before Miss Lata could say anything, Lani went for it, saying, 'Miss, all I want to know is, why are the "Real Sāmoans" so angry and mean?'

'Okay, mālolo everyone, just relax for a sec.' Miss Lata needed a breath.

'So first of all, I can't speak for your parents, especially since I don't know all the details or their side of the story. But I want you to have a think about this. Teuila, you are right, we do live in two worlds and this has been an issue since pālagi people first came to Sāmoa ages ago. But what exactly is stopping you from being islander? If you believe the pālagi teachers don't get it, then how could you help them get it?'

Teuila paused for a moment in thought. But before she could reply, Miss Lata continued. 'Now, Masina, have you ever asked your dad what he has against Art? Especially since you are obviously achieving well above in all your subjects? Have you even explained to him some career pathways through Art? One thing I definitely know about Pasifika parents is that they have the highest expectations for us and do everything out of love, but they don't necessarily know how to communicate that all the time – because remember, they most likely were brought up the way they are trying to bring you up, and don't realise your environment here in New Zealand is a whole lot different.'

Masina instantly felt a little bad about all the things she'd said, and had kept saying in her head, about her parents, especially her dad. She didn't know the why, and was never told the why. Just the *Do what I say* part and, to be honest, she was still freaked out by the idea of talking to her parents about anything, let alone the eleventh commandment that she kept breaking.

Miss Lata moved on to Lani. 'So, what's a "Real Sāmoan"?'

Just then there was a knock at the classroom door. They all turned to see who it was. Vai stood in the doorway, a little startled to see all the eyes on her at once, especially the pair giving her evils and asking *What are you doing here?*

Teuila sensed the tension and said, 'Sau e nofo i o'u tafatafa – I invited Vai to our catch up.'

Lani kept her eyes on Vai as she sat in the empty chair next to Teuila.

'Malo, Vai,' Miss Lata said with a warm smile.

Vai sat in silence, like a third wheel, trying not to draw attention to herself, but she could feel Lani's eyes stabbing at her, trying to keep her in her corner.

'Okay, back to what we were talking about. Where was I?' said Miss Lata.

Lani repeated, 'You asked what a "Real Sāmoan" is, Miss. Why don't you ask Vai, because according to her and her friends, I'm a plastic Sāmoan.'

Miss Lata got up from behind her table and brought her chair closer to the girls.

'Vai o le ā le mea na tupu i le lua vā ma Lani?' she asked.

Vai's anger levels rose rapidly. *This was why I'm here*, she thought. *To get told off for making the pālagi cry!*

'Sa faaali mai le fiapoto o Lani ia te a'u,' said Vai angrily.

'What are you saying? I'm a plastic Sāmoan and I don't understand, remember?' said Lani snarkily.

Miss Lata tapped both their tables to get their attention and said sharply, 'Aua le femisa a'i o oulua o teine Sāmoa e faamuamua le faalogo ma le faaaloalo!'

This got everyone's attention and made Lani simmer down immediately.

Miss Lata took a deep breath and said, 'First of all, there is no such thing as Real Sāmoans and or plastic Sāmoans. If you have Sāmoan blood running in your veins you are Sāmoan, we are not the judges of who is what and who isn't … We all come in different shapes, shades and sizes, brought up in different environments and with different experiences – O outou uma lava o teine Sāmoa'.

This time watching her tone, Lani presented her case. 'But Miss, she basically bullied me yesterday when you saw me, intimidating me because I don't understand what she's saying.'

With Teuila now translating what Lani had said, Vai replied, 'O lona manatu e sili atu 'o ia nai lo a'u, ona 'ou te lē mālamalama i le gagana igilisi.'

Teuila then turned to Lani, saying, 'She said she thinks you're better than her, because she doesn't know how to speak English that well.'

Lani couldn't contain her anger any longer and, channelling her loudmouth sister Sofia's spirit, yelled, 'What? I do not! I look at you like I'm scared of you!'

Silence instantly fell over the group. Lani never yelled, and even Vai was shocked by the sheer volume that came out of her little beige-tinted body. Lani had frightened herself a little as well.

A moment passed before Teuila said, 'Wow. You guys totally don't get each other, in the same way that the pālagi world and our parents don't get it.'

'Yeah, I see it too,' said Masina.

'Assumptions and miscommunication – or no communication – leads to misunderstanding, guys ...' Miss Lata paused.

With Teuila resuming her translator role for Vai, Miss Lata took a breath and said, slowly and carefully so everyone got the message, 'Everyone needs to know who they are –' she looked at Lani, 'to be proud of who they are –' she looked at Teuila, 'to gain some understanding –' she looked at Masina, 'so you can belong.' Her gaze finally fell on Vai.

Lani couldn't believe what she saw. Vai was trying to hide the teardrop building in the corner of her eye. Lani now felt like the bully.

Miss Lata passed Vai some tissues as Teuila broke the awkward silence. 'Guys, I think I've got an idea, but I need everyone's help, including yours, Vai.'

They looked up at each other, cautiously interested in knowing more. Teuila's taupou spirit was in full force, her hands creating images in the air; there was passion in her voice and in her brave plans. Miss Lata started writing as Teuila spoke.

The bell for the beginning of school echoed in the corridor as Teuila wrapped up her impromptu presentation and finished off the now lukewarm koko. They thanked Miss Lata, while confirming who was bringing what to their next catch up session on Monday.

As they started moving out of the classroom, Vai nudged Lani and said, 'Sorry yesterday'.

Lani understood exactly what she meant, and slowly replied so Vai could understand better: 'I'm sorry too … Do you like Teuila's idea?'

'Ioe, manaia le plan … Plan good,' Vai said, remembering that Lani couldn't understand Sāmoan.

Lani turned away for a moment, asking Masina how to say something, then quickly turned back to Vai saying, 'Faafetai lava Vai,' feeling proud that she'd spoken Sāmoan out loud, realising that it didn't sound plastic or pālagi at all.

CHAPTER 11

Staff Meeting

Across the Palisers High School staff room whiteboard was written *Māori and Pasifika Achievement* and a list of strategies the school was putting in place to support this. As the staff buzzed around the well-deserved Monday 3.00pm coffee and biscuits put out by their school leader, Mark Jensen, there was a knock on the door and a student asked for Miss Smith. It was Vai asking for a paper copy of the Journeys assignment, since they didn't have internet at home.

Eliza Smith looked a little irritated, saying that Vai should have mentioned this when she reminded them about it in class last week. Then she sent her to the office to collect the printout.

Eliza returned to her comfy seat in the corner of the staffroom, opening her laptop to print the requested document. As her syndicate team members, Nilau Lata and Luke Grainger, took their allocated seats around her, she turned to her tea and bikkies as Mark started the meeting.

'Welcome, everyone,' he said. 'We want to start off with our usual sharing of good practice, our progress, and challenges we are experiencing specifically around positively impacting Pasifika achievement, since we have highlighted this as a real need to focus on for this second half of term two.' He continued to provide examples of effective strategies: Knowing our learners – Developing Positive Relationships, Cultural Understanding, Engagement and Motivation.

'So let's start this week's feedback session by discussing and sharing amongst your departments first, then report back to the rest of us in about twenty minutes, as we also need to go over last week's learning conference outcomes. Thanks, everyone.'

Teachers began turning chairs towards their teams. Chatter slowly built in volume as one by one, teachers shared their experiences, trials and successes with their students. Luke Grainger was the Geography veteran who knew everything there was to know about places, land, locations, inhabitants and all of Earth's phenomena. So it wasn't a surprise that he started by sharing that the Pacific Islands is made up of Melanesia, Micronesia and Polynesia, reminding his team that Māori are in fact also part of the Polynesian group.

He then added that the Pacific Islanders in his classes were from the Polynesian group, that he'd had success incorporating geographical tasks based around the Pacific Islands, and that the increase in engagement was 'very pleasing'. This then led into some of the challenges he was up against, like one of his students, Lima, 'not completing his work because of his small amount of English, which affects his understanding.'

As head of department and Senior History Studies

teacher, Nilau Lata noted Luke's feedback down on paper, and they discussed the possibility of Nilau helping to translate instructions for students in Luke's class and giving Luke some basic language lessons, which she happily agreed to.

Next was Eliza. She talked about how she'd been encouraging her Pacific students to be experts in her classes throughout the term, so that they could be leaders of their own learning. She then proudly talked about her Journeys assignment as a way of getting to know her students and their families better, and how, due to a student's query about Pacific history, she wanted to include this in their school's cultural week, once the date was confirmed – something she wanted to talk to Nilau about.

Eliza's challenges were quite similar to Luke's. Some of her Pasifika students weren't completing work, and due to family and sporting commitments there seemed to be a lack of participation by some of her Pasifika students in general. She mentioned Vai, saying she didn't know whether she was listening half the time, and gave the example of how she'd only just asked for a hardcopy of the assignment, which had been given out last Monday and was due in two days.

The next teacher was Nilau. She turned her screen to her two team members and explained that she had been working on developing and strengthening relationships with her Pasifika students by not only checking in with them regularly about school work, but also to find out what had been happening in their lives, '… which we all know can definitely impact their moods, efforts and progress with their learning.'

She carried on explaining how these relationships, and regular student feedback, had become the basis of what and how she taught in her classroom, as well as a way to get to know the up-and-coming junior students. She said she'd like to share footage of some Pasifika students taken today, as they gave her feedback about what worked for them, the challenges they faced, and how they were finding learning in general.

Eliza and Luke moved closer to the edges of their seats to get a clear view of Nilau's laptop screen, eager to see the little video presentation.

At the press of a button, Vai appeared on the screen. At first she seemed a little nervous about looking directly at the camera, but became more relaxed as Miss Lata asked the questions. Captions in English at the bottom of the screen translated what was being said.

The first question Nilau asked was, 'What helps you learn and what can help you learn better?'

Vai: 'Oute lē fiafia i le ā'oga. Oute lē mālamalama i le faiā'oga ma le gagana igilisi ... E vave le tautala a le faiā'oga ae lē fesili pe ua ou mālamalama. Ou te faafetaia i la'u uō o Lani ua maua ai lo'u fesoasoani.'

(Caption: *I don't like school because my English isn't good and I don't understand … Some teachers talk too fast and they don't ask me or check that I understand. Thankfully my friend Lani is going to help me with my work.*)

Eliza and Luke were glued. Both were taking their

own notes, but a hint of sadness appeared in Eliza's eyes as she watched Vai on the screen. She felt bad that she had just been moaning about Vai a few minutes before.

The next segment showed Masina, who seemed quite excited to be filmed. Before Miss Lata could ask her question, Masina let loose. 'Do I like school? Yes, I do, but I don't love it. I know it's important and will help me, but it's been drummed into me that I need to go to university by my parents who are uber hard-core, especially Dad being a minister – this actually makes me annoyed because I love Art and he despises it, so that's why I keep it a secret, but yeah, that's a whole other story … oh yeah, what would help me learn better at school? I guess more challenging assignments or activities, and I actually hate being asked 'islander' questions just because I am one … plus I don't know everything, I wasn't even born there, and honestly, it just makes me think the teacher doesn't know or want to know because we're there to be like their cheat sheet or something why can't they learn for themselves…' The screen went black as she was cut off before she could rant further.

The final segment featured Teuila, who explained, 'It's so frustrating that my last name – Ekanesio – is said wrong every time, and some teachers think I am Tongan when I'm actually Sāmoan.' This instantly made Eliza sit up straight. 'So this makes me think about how unfair it is that us Pasifika students have to say everything correctly in English and we get marked on it, while those whose first language is English don't have to speak our language or say our names properly … It's just like being told that we can look at Pacific History in culture week, like that's the only place it belongs – so does that mean I can only be Sāmoan when it suits the school? In one of these weeks?'

Miss Lata asked her final question. 'Well what can you do about this, and what do you think teachers can do about this?'

With determination in her eyes, Teuila said, 'I want to start a Pasifika student leadership group where we can talk about these issues and work on solutions with the school. I've already got some other Pasifika students interested, and the first thing we want to do is start a Pasifika cultural group where we share and celebrate our Pasifika cultures, through song and dance first, maybe. We would open it up for everyone to join – it could be an easy way to help others to develop their understanding of Pasifika cultures, our values and views as well as giving our Pasifika students leadership roles too, like Vai, who has volunteered to be a tutor. The best part is that it'll help us to be ourselves all the time ... As for our teachers, we want you to really get to know the real us. Our names, our cultures, our history and our languages. It all should be part of our school all the time. Teach it or learn it with us. This will help us feel like we belong and we'll know that you value us and who we are.'

Eliza was silent, while Luke, obviously chuffed, said, 'Wow, Nilau, that was great – hearing it from the horse's mouth that they want us to get to know them, and it'll help them and us include what they want for our programmes. I think I definitely need to get more feedback and student voices, especially from the students I'm struggling with –

what I can do to help them finish their work and even help them to better understand what's required of them. You definitely need to share this with the whole staff.'

Nilau smiled and said, 'It was the girls' idea to give us feedback on how they feel, but in a safe way, as they were raised, like most Pacific Islanders, not to "talk back" or question teachers, even if we ask for it … That's why it's even more important to connect, and to develop trust and an open dialogue with our Pasifika students through the relationships we have with them.'

Mark's announcement interrupted their conversation: 'Okay, team, let's finish up our conversations and start feeding back to everyone.'

Eliza turned to Nilau, saying, 'I feel so bad. I had no idea what I was doing or not doing – how they felt.'

Nilau could sense the internal processing and guilt building inside of Eliza, so she squeezed her arm whispering, 'No one knows until we build these relationships, give them a voice and learn who they really are and what they bring to our classrooms … only then can we really figure out what they need ... and it sounds like they need us to see the real them or help them to be the real them – just supporting them to be themselves, whatever that is.'

There was a brief moment of silence before Eliza finished the conversation, whispering, 'I want to know and learn more. I can definitely support them – do you think they need any help with the Pasifika student leadership group they're putting together?'

Nilau smiled, whispering, 'Absolutely – that's exactly what they want.' As Mark asked for each department's feedback, Eliza raised her hand, wanting to share her light bulb moment.

CHAPTER 12

End of Year Prizegiving

The principal, Mr Jensen, announced to the audience, 'It is now my great pleasure to welcome to the stage this evening Lani Sio, who will give the junior prefect report for the year.' As he stepped down from the podium, Lani took her place in the spotlight.

She smiled out to the audience, trying to avoid looking at her parents, who were waving at her from the crowd. She took a deep breath and let the Sāmoan spirit within her take over and fill the room. 'Tālofa lava, o lo'u igoa o Lani Sio. O lo'u tamā o Petelo Sio. O lo'u tinā o Sarah Sio. O a'u o le teine Sāmoa. Tālofa, tālofa, tālofa lava.'

She continued her speech in English, explaining the many school events and student achievements across the year, including the Pasifika student leadership group who'd successfully created the school's first-ever Pasifika group last term. It now had 56 members.

Petelo quickly caught the tear about to drop from the corner of his eye. The pride he had for his daughter, his teine Sāmoa, was overwhelming. He was glad that she'd talked to him about wanting to learn more, and that her new friend Vai was helping her. And he was pleased that he'd made the time and effort to help reconnect her to her Sāmoan roots, not realising that this was helping him and his whole family re-connect too.

As a family they had been learning, speaking and sharing more about Sāmoan cultural norms, values and language. Sarah felt less of an outsider by learning, being supported by Petelo and just being open to trying. She had even asked Petelo's sister Lupe to teach her how to make the ula loles that were placed on Lani's shoulders as she finished her speech.

Teuila and Masina looked on as Lani was embraced by her parents. Their hearts smiled for her, and both were hoping for the same from their parents as the awards started to be announced. English. Maths. Science. Social Studies. PE ...

The hall fell silent; Masina tried to focus on her own breathing. She was annoyed that her parents had found out about the awards through the stupid email newsletter. She'd hoped the internet would crash, or something. Nearly two whole terms had passed and she hadn't had a chance to talk to her dad. Well, she'd actually had plenty of chances, but fear and guilt had got the better of her each time, especially since she had joined the Art extension group without him knowing.

She couldn't help turning round to look at the small crowd of parents at the back of the hall. There. She spotted her mum. In a silent panic she saw the empty seat next to her. 'Please don't talk about the Art extension group, please Lord,' Masina prayed. Then Masina almost missed the announcement of her name as Teuila grabbed her arm, saying, 'Suga – you won'.

Masina looked up at the stage. Her beautiful artwork, based on her art inquiry topic of Tatau, was lit up on the stage for all to see. God must see everything, and he was making a point that karma was coming for her.

Masina's hesitant legs finally got the message to stand up and move along. As she did, she quickly scanned the audience for her dad. There. She found him, back turned and walking out of the hall. How was she going to face him? He was probably going home to pack up all her belongings and leave them on the front lawn. Her heart broke, but her well-trained fake smile hid her feelings.

On stage, Mr Walker, the Art teacher, stopped halfway through congratulating her as he looked down into the crowd. Masina followed the direction of his eyes to see a short man in an 'ie faitaga standing in the middle of the aisle, walking towards the stage. 'OMG, he is going to publicly drag me off the stage,' Masina thought. She held her breath.

Then suddenly, Masina's father was right next to her on the stage. He placed two hands on her shoulders and pulled her into a tearful embrace. The crowd went wild as Masina's tears flowed into his shirt.

Once the crowd had quietened down, Mr Walker continued, explaining that Masina's piece was entered into a competition and had won a prize that involved a free session with a graphic designer from Victoria University, for Masina and their Art extension group.

The crowd and Masina's friends cheered for her again, as Masina collected her certificate and medal and was escorted off the stage by her proud father.

Masina was still in shock as her father whispered, 'Miss Lata called me and told me you were getting the award, and I am so proud of you. I couldn't wait, so I went to the car to get you this.'

Wiping her tears, Masina took the rolled-up piece of paper and unfurled it, revealing the most amazing tatau design and pattern – a mirror image of the final malu her grandfather had done in Sāmoa on the taupou, Masina.

'Ou te fia talatalanoa iā oe pe a uma le laugatogi,' he said, smiling from ear to ear before Masina was rewarded with ula lei and showered with kisses by her mother.

Masina was still hypnotised by the drawing her father had given her as she sat back down in her seat next to Teuila.

'I love how our islander parents are no shame, aye, suga,' giggled Teuila.

Vai heard all the on-and-off cheering from the science lab she was cleaning with her mum. Vai and Sosefina were quickly trying to finish the room when Lani burst through the door. She acknowledged Mrs Amosa, 'Mālo tinā' before adding, 'Vai ta ō e sāuni.' She was obviously in a rush.

Vai's mum quickly followed Lani and Vai out of the class, remembering to lock the door behind her.

The evening continued with more special awards, then just before the final announcement, of the top academic award, Mr Jensen introduced a new award category, which recognised Cultural Leadership and Excellence.

'This student has shown a passion for sharing, supporting and teaching others about her culture, including our staff. She has also achieved excellence across all curriculum areas, and this is why we have decided to announce both her awards together. So without further ado, our first-ever recipient of the top cultural leadership award, and the winner of the top junior academic award for this year, is Teuila Ekanesio.'

Teuila's parents were already standing before Teuila could. She could hear their cheee-hooing as she quickly skipped up the steps to the stage. She thanked Mr Jensen and Miss Lata, who were each holding a trophy. Then, before Teuila could leave the stage, Miss Smith appeared on the podium in a light blue puletasi.

'Kiaora, Tālofa and warm Pasifika greetings to you all. My name is Eliza Smith and I am the Social Studies teacher for the juniors here at our school. I, along with a number of other teachers over the past two terms, have been supporting Teuila and the Pasifika student leadership group she has created. So on behalf of our group and our staff here at Palisers High School we would like to share an item as part of our "Taualuga", which is the final part of our ceremony this evening.

'I would also like to welcome to the stage and acknowledge an amazing Pasifika leader in the group – Vai Amosa, for teaching us all this siva, faafetai lava Vai.'

The empty floor space at the front of the stage became filled with bodies – Masina, Lani, teachers all in 'ie lavalavas, with Vai in her puletasi at the front. Teuila smiled

74

in excitement as she quickly joined in support with Miss Smith. Vai took her spot at the front and announced to the crowd, 'E faatālofa atu i le pa'ia ma le mamalu o lenei aso. O le a mātou faafiafia atu - Sāuni!'

Vai then led them into their pese as they gently swayed, softened hands painting a beautiful story of their journeys so far, guided by the proud teine Sāmoa spirits that were emerging and able to live freely.

And from the back of the hall, past the proud Sāmoan parents swaying and clapping in support from the crowd, Vai's mother, Sosefina, stood by the door, smiling at her daughter, thinking that the sacrifice had been worth it.

As the taualuga came to an end, an overwhelming feeling of pride came over Teuila's parents as they stood in the crowd, holding back tears as they watched their daughter, in awe of what she had created. A space where teine Sāmoa could proudly shine, be accepted as themselves, while helping others learn and understand who they were.

Then Teuila's mother, Mele, unconsciously scanned the crowd and realised that her daughter was teaching her parents something as well. That maybe the world was open to knowing and accepting their Sāmoan culture, and that her daughter might just have a chance to proudly succeed as herself, as a proud teine Sāmoa in this outside world too.

'A fia vave o'o lou va'a, alo na o oe,

ae a fia tuli mamao le taunuuga tatou 'alo'alo faatasi'.

(If you want to go fast, go alone,

if you want to go far, go together.)

-    Sāmoan Proverb

Teine Sāmoa Study Questions

Personal Reflection Questions

1. How did the story make you feel? Explain why.
2. What does this story make you think about and question?
3. Do you believe your cultural identity is important to help you and others to understand who you are? Why or why not?
4. What experiences have positively impacted your own cultural identity?
5. What experiences have negatively impacted your own cultural identity?
6. Do you feel like you are able to learn, progress or succeed as yourself? Why or why not?
7. What would help you to develop more confidence and understanding around your own and others' cultural identities at home and in school?

Character Questions

1. What is the most interesting thing you learnt about the main characters, Lani, Teuila, Masina and Vai?
2. Identify at least one main or minor character you could relate to in the story. Explain why.
3. Describe one way a student, parent or teacher changed in the story.

4. If you could give the parents and teachers in the story some advice, what would it be?
5. What are the characters learning about their lives and the roles they play in developing their own cultural awareness and understanding?

Setting Questions

1. In what time period is the story set. How do you know this?
2. Explain why the settings are important to the events in the story.
3. Could the story have taken place anywhere else? Explain why.
4. Describe a particular setting in the story and explain how it helps to create the mood during an important scene.
5. How much time passes in the story?

Plot Questions

1. What do you think is the most important part of the story and why?
2. Describe an event from the story and the impact it made on the characters involved.
3. Identify and explain an important idea in the story that is relevant to students, parents or teachers today.
4. Could the story happen in real life? Explain why.
5. Think of an important event. How would the story have changed if this event had not happened?

Theme Questions

1. What are the key messages about cultural identity in the story?
2. How does language relate to culture? What is needed to maintain our languages at home and in schools?
3. Explain one specific aspect of the Sāmoan culture described in the book and compare it with a culture you are familiar with.
4. What is cultural confidence and how is this developed within the characters in the story?
5. Describe two main themes in the story. Provide specific examples and/or quotes from the story to support your answer.

Conflict and Resolution Questions

1. What cultural challenges did Lani, Teuila, Masina and Vai each face in the story?
2. What cultural challenges did the parents in the story face?
3. Describe and compare Miss Smith's relationship with Teuila and Vai before and after the staff meeting.
4. How did Miss Lata and Miss Smith help their students in succeeding as themselves, as teine Sāmoa?
5. What are the key lessons from the story for Pasifika and non-Pasifika students, parents and teachers?

Author's Purpose and
Writing Technique Questions

1. Explain the use and purpose of the Sāmoan language in the story.
2. Why do you think the author wrote the story from the different viewpoints of the characters?
3. Who was this story written for? Describe the different target audience groups and justify your answer.
4. Explain the organisation of the book. How is it important to the development of the story?
5. The story begins and ends with Sāmoan proverbs. How do these Sāmoan proverbs connect to the story and how can they be applied to everyday life?

The Teine Sāmoa Project

Everyone has a story to tell.

Stories are filled with life experiences and lessons that transcend space and time. They have a universal power that helps us to reflect, and think critically, allowing a deeper understanding of ourselves, others and the world around us.

But the best stories are like mirrors. They reflect our lives and experiences, and help us to connect to the events, characters, and even the language used in the story. These stories let us know that we are seen, heard and are valued.

So as Sāmoan, as tagata Pasifika, where are our stories? Where are we in the worlds we live in? Where can our tamaiti proudly see themselves? Be heard? Feel valued? For well over a decade I have heard hundreds of stories from students, parents and educators who have been asking these same questions.

Students have shared with me their experiences of not knowing what being Sāmoan means, wanting to belong, while facing stereotypes, encounters with unconscious bias and racism, and being a proud teine or tama Sāmoa but not having their culture and identity valued outside of home and church. Educators on their own journeys of cultural identity talked about the ongoing challenges they faced personally and professionally, strategies they used to better connect with our Pasifika tamaiti and how they actively supported their non-Pasifika colleagues in better understanding our cultural values within their own school communities.

After writing teine Sāmoa the story, I stopped and thought - just imagine if there was a space for all to access and experience the power of *our stories*. Then maybe more people would be moved and motivated, like I was, to promote and develop the cultural awareness and understanding needed to encourage some much needed talanoa (conversations) between our tamaiti (children), 'āiga (family) and educators.

All this thinking led to the Teine Sāmoa Project.

A space created for teine Sāmoa to share their real life stories, their unique perspectives and voices that could be accessible to our own people and others within our communities. Stories that reflect us and help others understand us. Stories that prove the importance of needing to tell our own stories.

The following fourteen stories are from real life Sāmoan students and highly experienced Sāmoan educators. They share their personal experiences, challenges and lessons for us - Pasifika and non-Pasifika tamaiti, 'āiga and educators - to better support and enable our tamaiti to succeed as themselves, as proud teine and tama Sāmoa.

So as a result of the rich personal and professional experiences, talanoa and stories that have inspired this book and after years of searching and asking, where are we? I have realised that we have always been here and we have always had a voice. But I now know that it is only through telling our own stories that we can be seen and heard, allowing us and our tamaiti to be better understood and truly valued in the worlds we live in.

This is why *our stories* matter.

Telesia Tanoai

Year 8 Intermediate School Student

We moved to Taiwan from Wellington when I was nine months old for my mum's job. My parents sent me to a local school so I could be fully immersed in Mandarin Chinese, and at home they spoke to my siblings and I in English. Being raised bilingual, I listened for a long time. But by three years old I was speaking in both English and Mandarin Chinese.

My mum and dad are Sāmoan New Zealanders from Auckland. So every year we would go to Auckland to visit and spend time with my grandparents and the rest of my extended family. During one of these visits, my family and I went to church; apparently I saw Chinese people and my face lit up - I must have thought they were my people. I was basically a Taiwanese baby.

I even had a Chinese name, 杜天俐 DuTianLi, meaning 'God-given wisdom'. I spoke Chinese, I acted like my classmates, and I loved my friends but I knew I was different because I looked different. I was brown. I had different looking parents, and I was bigger than my classmates but I thought it was just normal. I even remember taking bigger bites out of my apple and wondering why my other Taiwanese friends didn't.

As I turned five years old my mum's job contract

finished and my family moved back to Wellington. Although fluent in Chinese, I went from a fully immersive environment to zero exposure. I gradually lost the Chinese language I knew.

I remember around my third year of school in Wellington I noticed a girl that looked a bit like me. She was brown, she could have been one of my cousins. I asked her at morning tea time what her name was and she said, "Te Onganaiti." I told her my name was Telesia, and that I was a Sāmoan, and she told me she was half Sāmoan, half Maori.

It must have been meant to be because during lunch I saw she took big bites of her apple like me. We became great friends, and we would go around telling people how alike we were. "We're both Polynesian, both tall, both like sports," Te Onganaiti would say, "and we both take big bites of apples!" I would add cheekily. It was so good to finally find someone who was like me and understood me.

Wellington was my new normal, and it felt like home.

Then one day my mum came home from work, and told my family she had been offered another job in Taipei, Taiwan. We were heading back to our home away from home.

Returning to Taiwan, I was so happy to be back. My dad had told me one of my old friends from kindergarten was attending the same school as me. I was really excited to see her, but when she came up to me, I couldn't understand what she was saying. Connecting with my kindergarten friends motivated me to learn to speak Chinese again.

I wasn't a baby or toddler any more, I was much older now. I had come from three years of schooling in New Zealand and it was so different. School started at 7.30 a.m., we had to change into indoor shoes (crocs) and I had a very strict teacher. If I forgot to put things away, didn't look tidy or have pretty handwriting, or just didn't do things right she would throw my work out the window or make me sit outside. Sometimes she'd even push my desk over making my books fly across the floor.

I also found it hard to fit in and socialise with my new classmates. I could sense people looking at me, then talking about me which was confirmed when I began to understand what they were saying. At school, I was given a nickname, "Brown Cheese." I was really hurt and I couldn't understand why they wouldn't accept me like before.

Luckily, school wasn't the only place where I could make friends. I was able to make really good, kind friends at Church. I could also relate to the children of my mum's colleagues, who like me, had grown up in different places around the world. But sometimes I would think about my friend Te Onganaiti. Maybe I would feel more at home in New Zealand with other Pacific Islanders, like her?

Then it got hard being around my own Sāmoan family during our annual trips to Auckland. I didn't know the Sāmoan traditions and customs that my cousins, aunties, and uncles knew. I felt stupid not knowing what was happening or what was going on. I couldn't speak the language, I couldn't tell when I was supposed to be doing something, or if I was doing something wrong. I acted differently because I was raised differently. I felt like a foreigner to my own family and sometimes I just didn't feel Sāmoan enough for them.

Then after four years in Taiwan, at eleven years old, my mum told us she had been offered a job in Suva, Fiji. I was relieved and excited, being Pasifika I would be getting closer to where I was from and could feel like I belonged.

But Suva was a culture shock. It was such a different world. My school was overcrowded and under-resourced. My sister even had to buy her own desk. Some classmates pointed out that I was different because of my upbringing in Taiwan. They would say, "You act white," which was new and confusing to me.

In Asia I was teased for being brown. In Fiji I was teased for being white. And within my own family, I felt not Sāmoan enough. I wasn't accepted and didn't belong anywhere.

Then after one year in Fiji, my family and I moved back to Wellington, New Zealand. At first I was not keen to move back and I begged my parents to reconsider. It had taken me a while to adjust to living in Suva, and in the end I was able to make friends with like-minded students who were concerned about climate change and passionate about climate justice. We called ourselves the Pacific Social Justice League. I also discovered dance and I had made good friends at one of the best hip hop schools in Fiji - Mata Dance school.

However, we moved back to Wellington, where we currently live, and I quickly remembered why it was my second home. I don't really stand out as much, and there are many people who can help me understand more about my culture. I think this is why I have been able to build my understanding of who I am instead of trying to constantly fit in.

Recently my sister and I entered a New Zealand film competition. My entry was a movie called *Brown Mirror*. It was about my experience of being a Sāmoan New Zealander who has lived in different places around the world and the struggles I faced with my Sāmoan identity. After it was launched we received so much love and support, which really boosted my confidence knowing that there are other people out in the world like me. It encouraged me to learn more about my culture and who I am.

All my life I've been told what I am and what I'm not. But what I know is that home is where my parents and sister are. Also that I am a teine Sāmoa – a label that I'm still getting used to and learning about. And just like the main character in my film says, "It doesn't matter how much Sāmoan blood runs through your veins, or if you speak the language, or if you live on Sāmoan land, you are Sāmoan." I tell myself this now wherever I go.

Trinity Tauaneai

Year 9 High School Student

I'm not your typical teine Sāmoa. I'm quite loud and proud about being Sāmoan and I love my sport. I feel like being Sāmoan is a bragging right and I've learnt not to be afraid to speak up for my culture if I have to.

Early on I knew sports would be for me, especially seeing my older siblings grow up through sport. My siblings and I also quickly figured out that we were only allowed out of the house for fitness or for sport, not to just 'hang out' or be with friends – none of that, so sports it was!

I started playing league when I was seven years old and I loved it. I then picked up softball as a summer sport at eight years old. But everything changed when I hit Intermediate School.

Thanks to my island family genes I had grown taller, bigger, faster and stronger which meant I was perfect for most sports. Then I added touch, netball and basketball to my list of main sports. I even made representative sides for all the school's sports teams as well as club league and club rugby teams. I've always been used to playing at least a grade up too. At twelve years old I was playing for our local High School rugby team alongside eighteen year olds.

It was all fun until I started noticing a few things.

First came the comments about my islander appearance like, "You've got big calves for a girl," or "You're big for your age." I still don't get why people just point out our differences and then follow it up with a joke about us islanders being big boned or liking our food. I can't help that I was built this way.

Next, I realised that teachers signed me up for all sports at school just because I was good at my main sports. They wouldn't even ask. They'd just tell me that I had a trial or training to go to. Some were sports that I never even put my hand up for. One pālagi teacher even told me, "You're going to burn out," and I was so annoyed with him because he was the one who put me down for all the sports without asking in the first place. So I guess they liked it when I helped them win, but when it looked like I was going to crash I was on my own. That's how it felt.

I even think some of my past teachers used me to look after the naughty kids in my class. I already knew a lot of the boys as I'd grown up with them and I knew most kids were scared of me because I towered over them. So I was often told to look after another student if they weren't doing what they should be doing or I'd be used as a threat to other kids if they didn't behave. It wasn't fair, I wasn't the teacher and sometimes I felt like I was being used because of my size.

Then came the people who assumed that I played so much sport because I only knew sport. That I wasn't intelligent and couldn't possibly be doing well in class. But what they didn't know was that I was in Maths and English extension classes, and I was a student councillor, a cultural leader, and I'd won sportsperson of the year as well as the overall principal's award at our Intermediate School. It was really hard but I wanted to do it just to prove that I could play sports and have brains as a teine Sāmoa.

On top of all of this, most people would say my surname incorrectly. I really began to notice when my name was always announced wrong in school assemblies and sports awards, which always came with giggling and teasing from others.

Thankfully I've now realised that a name is not just a name. Like so many Sāmoan names, my surname represents who I am and where I come from.

My grandmother, the heart of our family, taught me everything about the Sāmoan way of life, and told me that our name comes from my grandfather's village of Leulumoega in Sāmoa. He was a church minister and was well respected. Grandma told me that our surname is important because it represents my granddad and all the work he did within our village, as well as my ancestors and our family.

Knowing this helped me to develop the confidence to correct and teach people how to say my name properly. It has also helped me to be more confident and speak up for myself and my culture against the stereotypes we face and when people use us in a way that keeps reinforcing these stereotypes.

I think about all the people who I would not want treated this way. I think about my grandma, a strong and proud Sāmoan. My parents and my siblings. My cousins and my friends.

So when I stand up and speak out, it is for all of us, and it is something that I want to encourage all teine Sāmoa to do. How else will they know if we say nothing and keep allowing it all to happen?

So now that I am at High School I automatically correct and teach my teachers how to say my name. I openly point out generalisations that are made about my people, my culture and myself. Each time I remind myself about who I represent and what I am - a loud and proud teine Sāmoa.

Rebecca Sa'u

Year 11 High School Student

My dad gave me a Sāmoan book to read called 'O Lou Ala I Malo'. Inside the book was a chapter called 'O le Tama'ita'i Sāmoa' (Sāmoan women). It talked about how women are responsible for caring for the 'āiga (family), feau (chores), inside and outside of not only their own homes, but also the house of the faifeau (church minister). It also said that we should know how to lalaga fala (weave) and be able to do mea faasāmoa (Sāmoan cultural things) like the ava during an ava ceremony, as well as know what to do with 'ie toga (fine mats), and siapo (tapa cloth).

After reading the chapter, I closed the book and took a minute to think about my own teine Sāmoa life.

Being born in Sāmoa and raised in New Zealand as a church minister's daughter, there have always been expectations. Like most Sāmoan children, faaaloalo (respect) is at the top of the list, so *knowing* what to do to show faaaloalo to your parents, elders, matai (chiefs), and church ministers is very important. We are also expected to be examples and role models for other children within the church and even when we are outside of church, especially with everything we do reflecting on our family.

But then I realised that the chapter was missing something. It clearly talked about what to do in our homes, a church minister's house and even the house of a matai, but what about outside of our Sāmoan cultural world? In the pālagi world?

From what I've seen through school, many Sāmoan girls stop being teine Sāmoa because it's just too hard and I can see why - we are surrounded by pālagi and everything that is pālagi. For instance, I remember when I got chosen as part of a group to attend a special Maths and Science Masterclass lecture for my High School. It was not unusual for me to be the only Sāmoan in the group for these sorts of things, so I didn't think anything of it. But when I entered the university lecture theatre I was quite shocked to be the only brown face in the crowd of schools across the region that attended. I instantly felt small and intimidated as eyes followed me across the room to my seat.

I remember when I got home, I told my dad. "Don't be scared, it's good – you can show them that Sāmoan people, can do just as good," he said trying to build up my confidence. My dad is my number one supporter, he likes talking to me and my six other siblings, encouraging us to go for every opportunity we can in order to succeed as Sāmoan.

This is something that I think he has ingrained in all of us kids throughout our home, school and church life. For example, my siblings and I have taught other students and teachers about our Sāmoan language and culture, and we've fully participated in community and school cultural events like Sāmoan Language Week and cultural concerts.

Even some of my High School teachers encourage us to be Sāmoan, which I think really helps. Like my German teacher telling the whole class about her yearly trips to Sāmoa and discussing parts of our culture with us. Then one time we had a relief teacher who was pālagi and he allowed us to write a prayer in Sāmoan. He shocked all of us by reading my prayer out to the class fluently. This made me feel valued as a student in his class. It was such a proud teine Sāmoa moment.

But I must admit, the majority of teachers I've had are not like these teachers. At all. I've also had friends complain about their families, expecting them to act pālagi at school, so that they can go further in life. Like not being allowed to participate in anything cultural, not being expected or encouraged to speak the language or know anything about our culture. It's quite sad because I see these friends struggling to know who they are and who to be sometimes.

So when I look again at the book my dad gave me, I think about how much more challenging it is to be a teine Sāmoa, when we don't live in Sāmoa. There is so much working against us in the pālagi world, like some of our own families and teachers not being able to support and allow our Sāmoan identities to shine, making it harder for more of us to succeed while being true to who we are.

I guess this is what makes it even more important for us teine Sāmoa to know who we are, what we are, no matter where we are. And this is probably why every morning when my dad drops my siblings and I off to school, he says, "Focus and be yourself - just be yourself." And being myself is being a teine Sāmoa, who is not only proud of what she is but is also not afraid to succeed as herself.

Akenese McCarthy

Year 13 High School Student

It's so hard being a teine Sāmoa. You always have to be good. All. The. Time. Even when no one is looking, but that's never because God is always watching, my mum says.

I'm the oldest of five kids. So the bar is set extremely high. My parents like most island parents have really big expectations of me. Doing feau (chores), setting a good example, achieving at school, always having to listen, even when you're sleeping, and definitely no friends – just school, home and church.

My parents tell me to do this and do that, sometimes pushing me towards things that I don't even want to do, like going for Head Girl or telling me that I am going to University. But I know my parents love me. I know it's their way of showing their alofa and that they just want the best for me.

I also know they see a lot of potential in me, but to be honest, I don't always see a lot of potential in myself sometimes. I guess I haven't really learned how to do this. Sometimes I just feel like an islander robot being programmed with what to say or do, and that mistakes and failure are not an option.

So yeah, I know what I can do because I get told to do something and then I just do it, but I do sometimes think what for?

Just look at the world we live in. Like we don't have many Pasifika female leaders that I know of or aren't really taught about any, so where are our teine Sāmoa in these roles? From what I know and have seen in our society, it's really a pālagi thing to lead at the front and us islanders just seem to be always at the back or working underneath them somewhere.

Don't get me wrong, I do want to do well for myself, my parents and family but I feel like most of my life so far has been about people pushing their expectations and standards on me and sometimes it just gets too much. Like last year I fainted from exhaustion and anaemia because of all the pressure and stress of being a Poly group leader and the workload from school just got the best of me that particular week.

As a teine Sāmoa we are not really raised to express our own opinions which is probably why I find it hard to open up sometimes and can't always fully communicate everything. I think I come off as confident but a lot of us teine Sāmoa are good at putting on a front and acting happy. The reality is that I'm living an adult life right now - helping to raise younger siblings, feau, cooking, church, being still in Sunday School and I'm seventeen years old - so I'll probably still be doing Lotu tamaiti (White Sunday) when I'm in University!

Peoples' hopes and dreams hang on me and it's tiring and exhausting to live up to the image of being a teine Sāmoa that carries everyone with her wherever she goes - with a smile. But then I am also grateful for my parent's sacrifice, providing for us and teaching me life skills like how to do laundry, something I know heaps of kids my age don't know how to do. So I really do want to pay them back for everything because that's how alofa (love) works for us, I just wish being a teine Sāmoa came with way more support and understanding.

Most of my teachers have no idea about our teine Sāmoa world.

If I am late to school, it's because I'm actually exhausted and my life isn't like a normal teenager. I have a full schedule with helping to sort siblings, church obligations, sports on top of school work, so late nights are normal for me.

One time a teacher was concerned with my lateness and talked to me about seeing the school counsellor. She kept bugging me about it. Even though I knew she meant well (I told her I was tired and actually just wanted to be left alone), she still followed through with booking me into the school counsellor.

But if she really knew me, a teine Sāmoa, she would know that us islanders are not raised to talk to strangers, like counsellors, about our problems. Instead I needed her to believe me, understand my world, and ask me how she could support me, that was all. Not refer me to a stranger.

Honestly, if my teachers knew me they would know how much pressure and stress I am under. I wouldn't just be a pass mark to some of them. Instead, they would show they care by learning about me, my world and my culture which is really important to me.

You know I always never understood why we had to learn the pālagi way of things our whole lives and pālagi don't have to learn anything about our way of life and how we do things. Even something as simple as our Poly group – if we had more teachers involved who were properly supporting us (because it is important to us), it would help teachers to better connect with us and understand us.

And I don't know who told non-Pasifika teachers that using islander stereotypes is the best way to relate to us because it really isn't. Some of them don't even realise how offensive it is to make jokes about how islanders like to eat a lot, or about our Sāmoan feet, or they think that knowing the word "sole!" is enough to get our attention. Instead it actually shows the opposite, that they don't know us or our culture.

Plus, it all just proves that we have to go above and beyond – we have to work twice as hard to break these stereotypes and prove them wrong, as well as trying to keep up with the pālagi kids.

Great - another thing to add to my things to do list.

Sarah McLeod-Venu

Year 13 High School Student

I never really knew about culture and ethnicity throughout my primary school years. So growing up I thought I was just like everyone else. When I think back there were only a couple of times I thought we did things differently.

Like I remember having two separate birthday parties for my fifth birthday. We had only our immediate family with grandma and grandpa, aunty and uncle, a cake and presents on my mum's Scottish side. Then on my dad's Sāmoan side, I remember the house being full, it was a huge celebration like a twenty-first and there was simply more of everything – people, noise and food.

I've always had a strong connection with both my Scottish and Sāmoan family growing up. But my pālagi side was definitely quieter, calmer and simpler. My Sāmoan side on the other hand laughed out loud a lot, and had bright and bold personalities which celebrated everything and anything and were together all the time. Both sides of my family have always loved me, it's just that they show it in different ways.

It wasn't until I was at Intermediate School that I was told what I was. "You're an Afakasi," my family said. But I honestly didn't really know what that meant. I only knew that I was different.

One time I was a flower girl at my aunt's wedding and I had to learn a siva (Sāmoan dance). I saw that all my cousins were natural dancers – they understood the song, the actions, what to do and even how to stand. As part of the back row, probably to hide me as I wasn't as good as the other girls, I felt like my position. I felt behind, that I didn't belong or that they felt sorry for me because I was different. And I was.

I've also always had other Sāmoan friends growing up but when I hit High School I became distant with them because I found that I couldn't connect to what they would talk about. I didn't go to church or do Lotu tamaiti (White Sunday) like them, I couldn't speak Sāmoan, we spoke English at home, and it seemed like my parents were way more relaxed than theirs – all things that were repeatedly pointed out to me by 'real Sāmoans', as if I didn't already know.

The thing is I have always loved my Sāmoan culture, but I just didn't know a lot about it to feel that I would be fully accepted by Sāmoans as Sāmoan. Although I did find the pālagi world a lot easier to fit in, probably because I looked more like them, I still didn't feel like I belonged with them entirely either.

I really felt stuck because I couldn't fully relate to the islanders, with my pālagi side being highlighted, reinforcing that I was different. But then I also felt that I wasn't pālagi enough for pālagi, because I was always proud of being Sāmoan. I was in a constant tug of war - adjusting and changing for who I was around, the situation or environment I was in. This was when I felt the most lost because I couldn't be myself and I didn't even know sometimes what being myself was.

It wasn't until I was a senior at High School that I started embracing my afakasi-ness.

I think it all came from realising how lucky and grateful I was to have both parents supportive of each other's differences and cultural backgrounds. Mum had learnt some Sāmoan language and always encouraged us to learn about our Sāmoan culture. For example, when we go to family events she always wears 'ie lavalavas, always offers to help and supports my aunties in the kitchen, and organises family events. Although she was different, she embraced the culture and she was accepted as 'āiga (family). She knew how to work the worlds she lived in. So could I, I thought.

This is why I've made it my lifelong journey to learn more about my Sāmoan culture to help me feel more confident in my Sāmoan world. Knowing our Sāmoan language is a big part of this and my brothers and I plan to return to Sāmoa to start a family construction company one day. So learning what it means to be Sāmoan has become our journey as a family, with the support of our parents.

I've also now realised that having two cultures can be an asset and my role as Head Girl at my school has proved this. By being more than one culture, I think I am more accessible and approachable to islander and pālagi students and teachers. I actively support and represent diversity in our school and aim to use my different cultural experiences to connect and relate better with more people. I have a lot of our islander students ask me to help them with the best ways to approach pālagi teachers or situations and I have even had some pālagi teachers ask me about connecting them with students who could support certain Pasifika events within our school.

I also know of full blooded Sāmoans who are at the same stage as me culturally, trying to learn more about our culture in order to feel more confident and accepted as who they are. This is why my hope is for our families and teachers to understand the challenges afakasi, Sāmoan and Pasifika students face so they can fully support us on our cultural identity journeys.

Angela Milovale

Year 13 High School Student

My pālagi History teacher gets me. He is married to a Sāmoan, so I guess that gives him a bit of an advantage. He speaks to us in Sāmoan, in parts – okay only a little bit and yes it comes off a bit plastic but at least he's trying. The best thing is that us islanders know he is trying just for us. He's making the effort. Like he greets us with, "Tālofa!" (hello) and asks, "o ā mai oe?" (how are you?) One time on a stormy day he even asked if I was "mālulu" (cold) and even though my friend and I cracked up we thought it was pretty cool.

Another thing he does which really helps me is to include material and topics that relate to us islanders. We have been studying the Dawn Raids this term, which I didn't even know about. He told us he wanted to learn more with us about our community and history, and that it was important to know more about ourselves as islanders, who we are, and where we come from. I think this was the first opportunity I had ever had to study my own history. It helped to strengthen my understanding of who I am and since it was taught to our whole class and assessed, it felt like it counted - that I counted, and that me and my history were important.

I even shared with him my goals of achieving excellence in History, and we did it. I say we because he really helped me. He was always there to answer my questions, no matter how random they were, and he never made me feel dumb. Instead he has always made me feel like I could get through work that I didn't always understand. It's like nothing is impossible and I feel like I can do anything I put my mind to a lot more now.

When I think about it, he's so approachable because the relationship we have is kind of built on a mutual respect we have with each other. Since he tries and keeps trying to get to know us, we feel comfortable knowing that he has our best interests at heart and he will always have our back – something that is definitely missing with some other teachers.

Earlier in the year, I had a teacher who I would never go to and ask questions because she taught like everyone automatically knew what she was talking about by explaining it once and then expecting us to finish the work straight away afterwards.

She wouldn't break the lesson or information down and she definitely did not make us feel that we could or should ask questions. My island friends and I would pretend that we knew what we were doing because we were afraid of her. Then she would do her walk around the classroom helping pālagi kids who seemed fine with her cold style of teaching, and then she would just move on to the next topic. Us Pasifika kids felt left behind, and below the pālagi kids who understood it.

But my History teacher on the other hand, it's like he knows what we will struggle with before he even gives us work, and makes it easier for us to understand. He does this by explaining, then showing us, then emphasising the important parts and following up with all of us in groups and individually. It's like he's on a mission to talk to all of us to make sure we understand everything.

I'm also really lucky that I have other teachers I can go to as well, like my Health teacher who is Tongan. She understands teenagers, relates to us and our problems with friends, school and home. We always compare and laugh about our island upbringing and she kind of gives us advice on anything as she's been through it already with strict parents, rules, and high expectations. It's like she's the teacher who will be there for us for anything we need, not just for school but all different parts of our lives.

Then there's the English teacher, who is Sāmoan. I've never been in her class but as a cultural leader she's the teacher who steps in to help me organise all the cultural stuff. She supports us islander leaders and students. She checks up on us and our grades when she doesn't have to (for most of us she's not even our teacher). But this is what makes us feel like 'āiga (family) as she actually goes out of her way to look out for us. This tells us that she wants the best for all of the Pasifika kids in the school.

So when I think about it, I realise that all the teachers who get us islanders and really help us in our learning are those who are islander or connected to an islander. I really wish this wasn't true, but it is.

If I was a teacher and wanted to relate to Pasifika kids better, I'd be asking these teachers who do know how to, because wouldn't it be pretty cool to have ALL our teachers know us, understand us so that we can do better at school?

I think so.

Tuto'atasi Vailalo

First Year University Student

Tassie

Tasi, but with an extra "s" and an "e"

because you see, they're not like you and

me.

My reflection stares back at me,

asking who am I meant to be?

Yes, I'm Sāmoan but I'm also Kiwi

at least that's what the world keeps telling me,

as I grow up searching for

my identity.

My name is Tasi but with an extra "s" and an "e"

Pālagi label to help a brown girl like me.

This was how I was colonised legally,

but the story my skin tells is of my Nafanua ancestry

and Sāmoan spirits that keep calling

me

to fulfil my original destiny.

My path already laid out in front of me

This planned pālagi route keeps leading me,

away from

me.

9 a.m. start and 3 p.m. finish,

as my book smarts went up my culture smarts diminished.

I studied, I was bright,

I made sure I did everything white.

They pushed to make me succeed in a system that was,

not designed for

me.

No sense of belonging,

it felt like I had no authority

'Plastic Sāmoan', I owned that title proudly.

But it then soon snuck up on me

'Teine Sāmoa' was completely foreign to

me -

Foreigner in my own country.

My name was the only thing that made us the same,

the extra "s" and an "e" in my name.

A constant reminder of who I'm not meant to be,

these two letters completely

derailed

me.

From my culture, my language,

my identity.

As I began to question,

Where is

What is

Who is

this teine Sāmoa called

Tasi.

Culture:

The ideas, customs and social behaviour of a particular

people or society,

discovering my own became

my priority.

But my own say, know our culture, know our language,

remember it all,

wishing my own cast the first safety net home.

Warning ahead, be careful not to fall,

the journey is so much different from the call.

Tālofa and tofā are some of the few words I knew

as I compared myself to my own thinking,

"Why am I not like you?"

I don't know the language,

I want to come home.

But with my ancestors' courage,

I need to come home.

I will voyage like they did,

I am coming home -

To my culture, to my language, to my people,

I will learn all there is to know

because I will not be waiting for the long return home.

I've lived in the same place,

looking everywhere for my face.

The ocean is our people's foundation,

but the cause of my separation.

From my people and my land,

but I soon came to realise that knowing my culture
cannot be found in palm trees or the sand.

Tutoʻatasi. No more extra "s" and an "e"
but independence, courage, and security.
This teine Sāmoa
now knows deep down inside
she is on this journey for the rest of her life.
In discovering my Sāmoan cultural identity
I am working on decolonising
me.
Learning who she is and that we are beautiful gems made
from brown island pearls,
just trying to find our way in this whitewashed world.

My name is Tutoʻatasi. No extra "s" and an "e"
like myself, culture is not static
but is changing across time and through
me.
My culture is not skin deep; it flows through my veins.
Never will I lose you, I now know inside,
reborn with my Sāmoan culture as guide
There's no need to run, no need to hide,
I will take back what this world has taken from
me
because I choose to succeed as who I'm meant to be.
Finally, for the first time I am free
Knowing, who I am,
where I'm going,

as the real

me.

Tutoʻatasi.

Makerita Feite Tago

Primary School Teacher Aide
Twelve years in Education

My dad was in a band. And my earliest memory was being two or three years old, sitting and listening to my dad's band practises. In his younger days he composed songs for different churches back home in Sāmoa - Ekalesia Faapotopotoga Kerisiano Sāmoa (EFKS), Mormon, Methodist. And he had taught himself to teach piano and guitar all by ear.

So growing up with no English allowed in our house we were always singing pese Sāmoa (Sāmoan songs) and performing siva Sāmoa (Sāmoan dances). Even for lotu tamaiti (White Sunday) my dad was always writing songs and directing performances.

Dad also personally knew some popular Sāmoan singers and groups like Tiamaʻa and Punialavaʻa. So due to this and because of his own composing, dad had always taught us the importance of remembering when singing or performing a siva, "You are singing or telling a story - someone else's story. So you must give it the respect it deserves by knowing what that story is about by learning and understanding the meaning behind it." This is something I have always remembered.

My dad's love for his music rubbed off on me as it naturally led me down the path of Siva Sāmoa and performance. I guess like him, performing has always been more of a passion for me, rather than a profession.

This is why after High School I attended Whitireia Performing Arts School. Although my parents were proud of my love for my culture, they were still concerned thinking that there was no job for this in the pālagi world. But with their wary blessing, I ended up discovering a world that was in demand for our Polynesian cultures and dances.

As part of my studies, I had the amazing opportunity to travel to cultural festivals around the world, performing four to five shows some days. This was a pretty exciting time of my life. I met so many different people and cultures who were so interested in our culture - we were like rock stars to some of them, drawing the biggest crowds and requests to perform at extra events during our tours. And by the end, I had gained a qualification in Siva Sāmoa, Cook Island dancing, Kapa Haka and contemporary dance, having travelled and performed in Canada, Belgium, Holland, England, Taiwan and Thailand.

I was also teacher aiding during my studies, so it was quite natural for me to combine my love of tamaiti and my passion for performance. I found that there was a need to support different schools with cultural programmes and in some schools I helped them to start their very first Pasifika or Poly group.

I was really eager and it was great, at first.

Like it was exciting that our culture was being welcomed and accepted into these schools, but I didn't realise this meant being left alone to do all the work myself with twenty to sometimes thirty kids. Feeling excited, one principal gave me the usual run down of the time, day, space that I would be working in with their group. Then by the second week, she was checking in like a probation officer to see what we had done and if all items would be learnt by the time Education Review Office (ERO) visited later that term.

Then year after year, I saw how these different schools were very proud and acknowledged for celebrating our Pasifika cultures due to the groups and language lessons I was teaching their classes, with little or no help from staff. Something that I honestly did not expect. Staff members showed that they were not part of the cultural and language learning aspects within their schools as they sat in assemblies, powhiri, and performances not knowing their own school pese or waiata, haka or siva. It was like they were guests and not actually part of the school.

This was really strange to me because in our culture, we all participate and support anything that is good for our 'āiga (family) or group. And since pese and siva are the usual go-to for including and exposing others to our cultures in schools, I couldn't understand how schools and staff loved it and the results from what I was doing, but weren't able to be involved or develop their own understanding by learning themselves so they may continue programmes without me. This was the hardest part.

It all reminded me of my dad and what he said about our pese Sāmoa and siva Sāmoa, "You must give it the respect it deserves by knowing what that story is about by learning and understanding the meaning behind it." Our pese and siva are representative of our Sāmoan culture and by learning with your students, teachers can gain a real understanding of our ways, our cultural values and beliefs because there is so much richness in our pese and dances. They not only make for beautiful performances, but the power comes from the storytelling and meanings behind the actions, the words and alagaʻupu (proverbs), something that I believe would be of great value to all students and teachers. This is also why I believe all schools should have qualified and experienced Pasifika advisors and tutors.

I've heard people say that they do not have school cultural groups because there is no one to take it or that there are not enough tutors to support schools and staff. But I think that we're really lucky to live in a time where it is possible to access our pese, siva and even tutorials through the internet, YouTube and Coconet – just to name a few. But I do still think the best way is to reach out and seek support from your own Pasifika communities and even local churches because isn't this what ʻāiga (family) engagement is all about?

Then the next step is not to just leave it to them, but to learn from them so that our culture can continue long after staff and Pasifika families move on to other schools.

And if Maori and Pasifika cultures are really valued by our schools, cultural group tutors or advisors should be paid for their cultural knowledge and expertise. It is really obvious that there is a need for us to provide cultural programmes of song, dance, language and even performance within schools, for students, but more importantly for teachers as well.

When schools have cultural performing groups they are telling their Sāmoan parents that we acknowledge and welcome who you are, and when staff are fully involved and learning about our culture through pese and siva Sāmoa it shows all of us that you are accepting and valuing us.

I remember a student smiled excitedly as she told me, "I've never danced outside of my home and church before." This is something I will never forget. This student was able to find a home away from home through our pese, siva, language, the meanings and stories behind it all.

So now as a general manager of a before and after school and school holiday programme, I have used my teacher aiding experiences and love for cultural performance, arts and events to emphasise the importance of embracing each other's cultures and helping our tamaiti and my staff to value their own by learning, understanding and truly valuing it together.

Eleanor McLeod

Primary School Teacher
Twenty-two years in Education
Nineteen years as an Intermediate Teacher, BEd
Senior school lead teacher, PB4L Coach and Facilitator

We weren't taught our Sāmoan language, much to our and others' amazement and disappointment. I'm sure my parents thought we'd learn about faasāmoa (the Sāmoan way) by osmosis. Things were never fully explained to my brothers, sister and I. We were meant to just accept it and not question anything. Whether it was to do with church, our family, or especially education – we were to get it done, make no fuss, pass our grades, and get a job. It was the norm, our Sāmoan born parents chose to conform and fit in which is why I became a product of my environment and my community, hardly teine Sāmoa material.

I had Maori and islander friends and I learnt more Maori than anything islander. Like many other Kiwi kids, I too learnt Maori waiata and I remember a new friend at Intermediate School asking me which iwi (tribe) I belonged to. "What do you even mean by that?" I remember thinking to myself. It's only now that I can joke with others and say, "Ngati Hamoa."

I remember as a youngster having a conversation with my mum about my future career path. A photographer, mechanic or perhaps a teacher? But in all my time as a student, I had never been taught by a Pasifika teacher, let alone a Sāmoan one. I had never known what it was like to have someone who looked like me, or had an inkling of what it was like to grow up like me.

My primary school report comments read, "Eleanor possesses leadership qualities but needs to learn when to use them." These comments were quite common and later in my teenage years it finally dawned on me that maybe I should pursue a career to make use of these leadership qualities. Teaching seemed to fit the bill.

I entered the gates of my first teaching job as an eager twenty-two year old teacher of a Year 7 & 8 class. There were thirty-one mainly brown faces waiting for me that day. Some friendly faces, some tough, some anxious, some excited, but all willing and waiting. The school was situated in a suburb whose face has changed over the years due to the large number of state houses in the area which housed Pacific minority groups and in particular, a quickly growing Sāmoan community.

As a Sāmoan educator I naturally gravitated towards my Sāmoan students, who had a strong background in faasāmoa. They all had very strong family and church connections. They knew who they were and were proud of it – praying, singing, playing and teasing one another in our Mother Tongue. These kids challenged and inspired me. They were true products of our beautiful Sāmoan culture and fluent speakers of our language. And at the same time, reminding me that I was not.

I even remember my Sāmoan students talking to our one 'true' Sāmoan teacher, Fia, about anything and everything, while I stood there nodding my head as if to say, "Yeah, I totally understand what you're all talking about." When of course I didn't, but I desperately wanted to.

It ended up taking me years to finally say aloud that I wasn't a fluent speaker. But once I was able to admit this to myself and then to others, I allowed myself to stop pretending and stop standing in the shadows behind the 'true' Sāmoans. I was more open to learn and the opportunities followed, like my own students offering to teach me Sāmoan.

I was also very blessed to work alongside some amazing teachers. Although the majority of my colleagues were pālagi women, they were real change-makers in education, outside-of-the-box thinkers and teachers who pushed and demanded the best of their students, who were mostly Sāmoan.

It was through these years that I was able to finally make the all-important cultural connection with my students. I learned alongside them and I was following best teacher practice around developing cultural understanding and connections with my students to better support them. But I still felt something was missing.

So after nineteen years my husband Scott and I decided to uplift our young family and make the move to Sāmoa. The Motherland, the place where I could be connected to my ancestors, my nu'u (villages), my 'āiga (family), my language and my culture - finally know who I am and where I am from.

Arriving in Sāmoa, I felt like my eager twenty-two year old self again, but this time ready to develop my own cultural understanding and identity as a Sāmoan. Then reality hit! All was not what I had hoped and dreamed of.

The school I taught at was a first choice school for many of the more affluent families of Sāmoa, expat families from New Zealand and Australia, and families from other countries from all over the world who come to Sāmoa for varying work commitments and opportunities. So the most shocking fact was that the majority of Sāmoan students were not fluent speakers of the language. I had assumed that here in our Motherland everyone spoke Sāmoan all the time. But I quickly learnt that you can actually live in Sāmoa and not have to speak one word of Sāmoan at all. All business, a lot of schools and daily living is, or at least can be conducted in English. English ruled and the pālagi way of success was the goal. I was in total shock!

What made it worse was that some of our students were the descendants of the who's who of Sāmoan society and history. I used to read stories about some of their ancestors who helped build and create Sāmoa upon the values of faasāmoa. I was so saddened by the impact of colonisation and the fact that I was teaching the children, grandchildren, great-grandchildren of our Sāmoan heroes in their dominant language, which was English. So, I had to change my game plan.

Fortunately, my time at my previous school had

equipped me with the skills to be able to create units and topics of learning that integrated the importance of cultural identity, allowing our students to explore what makes them who they are and the importance of knowing where they come from. As part of our learning we researched Sāmoan history through texts, took trips to the National Museum and around Apia city locating monuments, and we had visits from family members of prominent Sāmoan figures who were able to give very personal accounts of those early days of Sāmoan independence.

Learning conversations were deep, meaningful and highly emotive, where often cries of "How could they (Britain, United States, Germany and New Zealand) do that to our people? They were human beings…not animals or slaves to be owned!" My students lapped up the learning, were more appreciative in the actions of their forefathers and were so much more proud of who they were which helped to develop our confidence in learning and using our language.

One of the most significant events that my family and I were able to participate in was the Sāmoan Independence Day march along with our fellow colleagues and students. To hear comments like "I feel like a real Sāmoan now!" from students will sit with me always. I loved the fact that Scott and my own tamaiti, Drew and Jackson, got to experience this too.

Marching past all of the dignitaries, I didn't realise how emotional it would be for me, to represent my parents and my brothers and sister.

Tears began rolling down my face. For the

connection to my culture I had been searching for all my life. For the impact of colonisation that was evident and living freely in my homeland of Sāmoa. For my own parents and 'āiga who had to assimilate into the New Zealand way of life by sacrificing our language and our culture – and for so many of our tamaiti today who are still searching for who they are as a result.

It has taken me a long time but due to my new confidence and understanding of who I am and why I am, I finally feel like I can proudly claim the label of being a teine Sāmoa.

And as I prepare for my return home to New Zealand, I realise I enter into another new chapter of my life. One where I will actively share my learnings about the real need to decolonise our education system, especially since real learning cannot happen without culture. Also that we all need to know and value who we are, and our tamaiti must be supported in succeeding as who they are, as teine Sāmoa and tama Sāmoa, in both my homelands.

Trisha Daniels-Sopoaga

Primary School Teacher
Eighteen years in Education, BEd, MEd
Syndicate Leader, Pasifika Liaison, Equitable Digital Access Project
Coordinator, School wide Digital Fluency Facilitator

When our Pasifika mātua (parents) were growing up they too were told that university and higher education was the only measurement of success, leaving little room for our own interests and strengths we have as Pasifika. Don't get me wrong, university is great but not everyone's desire or destiny is to be an academic, and in our world today many have proven over and over again that academia is *not the only* road to success.

With the focus on the end goal of getting into university and very little support or understanding on how to get there, it's no wonder why so many of our children feel like a failure when they don't achieve. And it's usually what their parents' goals are for them. But our world is calling for trades, creatives, and even our languages, which so many of our children lose because of the pressure to achieve the pālagi way, and usually results in many leaving our cultures behind.

So many of us are raised with the usual, "Just do what the teacher says," attitude. Leaving all the power and responsibility in the hands of the teacher which also highlights the need for our Pasifika mātua to develop a better understanding of schooling today, and how to best support their child's learning as Pasifika.

Take the subject of Writing for example. Many Pasifika mātua still believe it's a subject where kids simply write stories, the more pages, the better your story is. But it's not. Our children are asked to look at multiple genres across the year and are being assessed on a multitude of things like spelling, punctuation, grammar, the words and ideas they select, use and organise. Then there's Maths which isn't just learning the rote way of remembering, the one way the teacher shows you to solve the problem. The focus is on strategies, sharing ideas and collaboration with others.

Then combine this with the reality that our Pasifika mātua receive a report, a 15-20 minute face to face check in once or twice a year, and due to our humble and respectful 'island manner' they tend to nod and agree with what is being said to them. Unaware or not knowing how to respond or ask questions for understanding or clarification from their child's teacher.

This is why I'm a huge supporter of initiatives like Talanoa Ako, PowerUp, Reading, Writing and Maths Together programmes. These initiatives really aim to support our Pasifika mātua by developing their understanding of different learning strategies across subject areas, their responsibilities, rights and roles they have in their child's learning journey. But unfortunately not all our mātua utilise these programmes within their schools for a number of reasons and miss out on a lot of learning tools and support for their child.

This is where I believe building and maintaining strong relationships with 'āiga (families) in our school communities is key to a Pasifika child's progress and success. And over the years I've found that there needs to be different layers of relationships, which together, encourage and empower our mātua with the right tools to do so.

At the core of everything is the relationships with our students. On top of our deliberate acts of relationship building, our Language Nest programme has been a huge help at our own school with developing stronger connections with our Pasifika students. This is where each week I take all our Sāmoan senior students to teach them about our Sāmoan language and culture. "Miss, I feel more Sāmoan, like I'm able to be Sāmoan," one student recently said to me. Our Pasifika mātua feedback was that they love their culture and Mother Tongue being valued by the school, beyond home and church, while learning that our culture can be a powerful asset beneficial to their child's future. Also there was an increased level of trust knowing there was an extra level of understanding to who their child is, and what they bring into the classroom.

The next layer of relationships involved developing staff cultural knowledge, so that they can be more understanding and receptive to our Pasifika families. For example, I regularly share my insights with them about how island families work - the importance of talanoa (conversations), using simple language, not just calling them when their child is naughty, celebrating successes and always working towards solutions and positive outcomes together. I even provide mini Sāmoan language lessons for my syndicate team around pronunciation, simple vocab, phrases and cultural perspectives to be integrated into their everyday classroom routines and planning. This is so our teachers can support the development of our student's Sāmoan identities, then we can help them to achieve as themselves.

It's also important that Pasifika teachers are not seen as the 'go-to' or 'one-stop shop' for everything that involves our Pasifika children and their families. Does it help that I am Sāmoan? Absolutely. I was raised through the alaga'upu - "E iloga le tama ma le teine Sāmoa i lana tu, savali, ma lana tautala" (A Sāmoan boy and girl is revealed by how they carry themselves, walk and how they speak). As a proud New Zealand born Teine Sāmoa I live and breathe my language and culture every day. But how will other staff build connections and positive relationships with our Pasifika community, if I am the only one who is always initiating and interacting with them?

I still definitely support staff when needed, like being a translator with our families, but our Pasifika parents want to see their own child's teacher putting in the effort to understand, relate and learn more about them. And not just when the Education Review Office (ERO) is on the schedule either. I can't see why we can't be actively learning about the different cultures in our classroom through something as simple as language. This should be happening all the time especially since teachers should be the biggest learners and models of cultural awareness and understanding in our classrooms.

Then there's the depth of the relationships we aim and need to have with our families. When we hear about our students' grandparents or a family member passing away, we always send a mea alofa (gift) on behalf of the school. When there are church fundraisers selling suppers, staff are always happy to support. We aim to treat our students and their 'āiga like we would our own family. It's that simple.

So it is through these levels of relationships that our Pasifika mātua respond to the 'S.O.S' signal we send out because we know they will show up and support us in the same way that we will show up and support them. This then makes for a safe environment for us all, teachers and parents, to share our knowledge, learn and develop an understanding of what we can collectively do to better support our children to succeed as Pasifika.

Luckily I work with a great team who understand that it's all about building a sense of belonging and community. One based on mutual trust, respect and open communication, which must be grounded in alofa (love). Because like the popular Sāmoan proverb says, 'E taui le alofa ile alofa; the love you give, is the love you get'.

Vaia'ua'u Pilitati

Intermediate School teacher
Thirty-seven years in Education
Fifteen years as Deputy Principal, DipT, BEd
Classroom Teacher, Syndicate Leader, Curriculum Leader

The first voices I heard coming into this world were Sāmoan. My parents were strong yet loving and as the eldest and only girl in the family I was raised to be a teine Sāmoa lelei, a good Sāmoan girl. These Sāmoan voices still remind me of my role to serve God first, then family, church and my students in my role as a teacher.

I adopted this Sāmoan voice with me as a fluent speaker of our language when I started school. No one at school knew I had a wealth of knowledge from my indigenous world. I was a real sponge at school. I silently watched everything. The teachers. The students. I had to learn how to speak English. I watched what they did, what they said, and how they did things, it was all so different from home.

My English improved and watching a lot of TV helped. I think that's why I have a slight American accent with an underpinning Kiwi twang. Over the next few years I fell in love with reading. Whenever I got new books, I couldn't wait to read them, using a torchlight to read during the car rides home at night.

I continued to watch and observe the bubbles I lived

in, one at home and one at school. It was very clear at home as a teine Sāmoa that my parents were my voice and at school I wasn't one to talk much in class anyway. I did the work like a good teine Sāmoa and most of my teachers never asked me anything.

Maybe they thought I was mute, or at least treated me like one.

At the end of my primary school years, I remember the 'hot pants teacher' – a female teacher who wore shorts in front of us, which was a very big no-no to us teine Sāmoa. My vivid memories of this teacher involved her standing in front of rows of pālagi students laughing, smiling at them and connecting with them. I wondered if I had to be white to have her smile at me? I sat at the back of the classroom with the Māori kids.

Then there was the 'office lady' at Intermediate School. She came into our class of thirty, and I noticed she started checking everyone's hair around me. I wasn't checked, she left without even looking at me. I sat silently thinking, why was I being left out again? It wasn't until later I realised, the office lady was checking for nits and I was the one who had them. I felt so embarrassed, ashamed of my huge puffy thick black hair.

The thing was that I knew I had a voice. I rehearsed conversations in my head every day – I just didn't know when to use it. And there were only a few teachers who collectively were able to unlock my voice.

Like my 'orange teacher'. At five years old this teacher took me under her wing, she introduced me to her rabbits and she gave me a bright orange fruit one day. She really cared for me.

Then there was my 'firm but fair Maths teacher'. At Intermediate School this teacher helped me to develop my love for Maths. She made me feel good about my abilities and I loved the proud feeling that came over me when I would finish the timetables questions and put my hand up first. She helped build my confidence.

Next was my fifth form High School 'ginger beard Maths teacher'. At the time you were given a score of one to five for the assessment system and I was only one of two students in the class who got a one! He always had the highest expectations of me and it made me feel good, that he could see me. The best part was that he always said my name correctly too. He made me feel respected and I felt like he valued me.

Finally, there was my sixth form 'inspirational Social Studies teacher'. I remember the conversation she had with me, "Have you thought about applying for Teachers' College?" I screamed in my head, "Are you talking to the right person lady?" Her words sat with me over the next year and I remember her positive and supportive spirit encouraging me, readying my voice for lift off.

I actually think I got my first job as a classroom teacher because I was a quiet, calm and well trained teine Sāmoa. I remember being told that I represented one per cent of Māori and Pasifika teachers in New Zealand at the time. I couldn't believe it. I decided to use this to help strengthen my voice. I had enough of my two bubble worlds silencing the voice I had and my journey to be heard began.

I remember telling myself, "Just say one thing." So in staff meetings, in syndicate meetings, in workshop groups, in any professional setting it was my goal to be heard. I still recall my heart pumping, palms sweaty, breathing heavily. I screamed in my head, "Just say one thing!"

After saying one thing, I would say another. I did this again and again. After years of observing I had learned the art of conversation and knew when to speak and how. This allowed me access to management and leadership opportunities, telling people about things that mattered to me and my culture.

I had found my voice.

One of my proudest moments of all time would be speaking at a Pasifika Educators' Fono. It felt great to collaborate and communicate with educators, schools, agencies and community groups on how to be effective when working with Pasifika students.

Now, although I had found my voice, I had learned early on that it didn't mean it was always going to be heard. I often found myself in professional situations where it was assumed I was not as qualified or as knowledgeable as my pālagi colleagues. My voice felt like it was being ignored again.

Like when I became a syndicate leader, we went on a class trip to the Botanical Gardens and an older couple approached the pālagi teacher aide and myself. I realised by their comments and questions that they thought the teacher aide was the head teacher in charge.

Then one time at a seminar for school leaders, I sat at a round table of pālagi professionals. From listening to the discussion across the table, which I was not invited to participate in, I realised that I was in fact the highest qualified person sitting at the table, which didn't really matter. Because it became obvious that my silence was received as not knowing anything.

All these moments made me want to be a better and different teacher and school leader, that would embrace all students and their voices. And I definitely knew that I never wanted any of our students to feel alienated because of the colour of their skin or being different.

My Sāmoan cultural values and beliefs are the essence of how I build relationships and who I am. It is my duty to serve with reciprocity, respect, belonging, family, trust, and compassion. I have been a professional observer all my life and I now know that it is a great skill and asset.

But I've also found my voice and the power of it. This is why my malaga, my journey, continues to empower, encourage and engage my teine Sāmoa sisters and tama Sāmoa brothers to support and amplify our voices - while at the same time, teaching others to listen to us and understand that our silence does not mean that we do not and should not have a voice.

Sinapi Faafetai Taeao

High School Teacher
Thirteen years in Education, MEd, GDipTchg (Secondary), BA, BSc
Whanau Head Teacher / Pastoral dean, Mathematics teacher

Once upon a time there was a teine Sāmoa. Born in Sāmoa, her parents decided to move their entire family to New Zealand, the land of milk and honey, to live a better life. She was constantly reminded of this – "We left Sāmoa for you," her parents would say.

She grew up in your typical Sāmoan household. As the eldest daughter she had to be a good role model for her two brothers. She had to do the right thing, no hanging out with friends after school or on the weekends, and definitely no boys. Her brothers seemed to have a lot more freedom, never receiving hidings or the responsibilities, duties and feau (chores) she had.

She realised early on in her life that she wanted to please her parents. This meant obeying everything her parents said, being compared to other teine Sāmoa to do as well or better than them, doing well at school and making sure that she was able to keep up with the demands of church and faasāmoa (the Sāmoan way) life too.

She became a 'people pleaser' and found it difficult to say 'no' to people in fear of disappointing them. She never wanted to be disobedient or be a failure at anything as she knew this would bring great shame upon herself, her siblings and her family. "So no mistakes allowed," she would tell herself.

So she finished High School, went to University and became the teacher her parents wanted her to be. With her three degrees (otherwise known as the golden tickets), she felt like maybe now she was finally enough.

Craving freedom, she decided to teach in Japan. For the first time in her life she was able to enjoy and explore the freedoms that she had been sheltered from most of her life – friends, parties, alcohol, boys. However, it still wasn't enough and she felt something was missing. Haunted by her parents' voices, "E iloga le tama ma le teine Sāmoa i lana tu, savali, ma lana tautala" (A Sāmoan boy and girl is revealed by how they carry themselves, walk and how they speak), she felt ashamed. She was not being the teine Sāmoa her parents had ingrained in her to be. She felt she had failed her family, and after five years of being away, she returned back home to teach in New Zealand at her parents' request.

As the only Sāmoan teacher at the High School she taught at, she knew she would have to work hard.

She loved her school but felt like she was not supported to learn and grow as a professional, being constantly denied opportunities to teach at different levels within her core teaching subjects. Then, when she used her own time, energy and money to create school wide initiatives that supported Pasifika students and raised the Pasifika profile of the school, there was very little support from the school itself. The feeling of not being enough grew.

Thankfully her connection to her students kept her

going. She saw their parents' high expectations they were trying to meet, their teachers' expectations that added to the pressures they were already under, and sometimes the school's low expectations of her Pasifika students.

Through regular talanoa (conversations) and developing meaningful relationships that went above and beyond, she was able to maintain high standards and expectations but support her students in achieving them. And by creating safe environments, where students could learn to take educated risks and make mistakes, she taught them about the importance of failure and resilience, and knowing how to get back up again.

She saw herself in the students she taught and was learning with them. She saw how fear, guilt and shame were not good motivators for our tamaiti and knew that her goal was to help them feel valued and develop their self-worth so that they could feel that they were enough, more than good enough. Something she realised and wished that someone had done for her when she was younger.

After receiving a Teach NZ Scholarship to complete her Master of Education, for the first time in her life, the teine Sāmoa thought about what she wanted for herself.

The life goals she created for herself involved promoting self-wellbeing and supporting our tamaiti to feel enough, alongside helping educators and our families to develop a better understanding of the importance of this.

Because this teine Sāmoa now knows that we need the time, space and support to develop our own expectations of ourselves instead of trying to constantly meet other people's expectations of us. And she now firmly believes that we can be successful as who we are when we know that we are enough.

Nila Uili

High School Teacher
Twenty-two years in Education, seven years as Intermediate School
Teacher, DipT, BEd
HoD of Junior Studies, Dean (Year 7-13), Director of Pasifika Achievement,
TiC Gagana Sāmoa, Specialist Classroom Teacher

My idea of what a good teacher is, has evolved over the years. As a child, the good teachers were those that made learning fun and introduced me to new experiences like eating waffles for the first time, hearing *The BFG* by Roald Dahl read aloud to the class, and singing songs.

In college, the good teachers were those that were passionate about their subject, whether it was Music, Science, or History. Their passion was contagious and you were inspired by it. They were also the teachers that saw the gold and potential in students, buried under layers of insecurities and fears. They believed in them and invested the time to seek out the gold, working with students to meet their full potential. One such teacher significantly changed the trajectory of my life.

It was the last term of my final year at college and I was panicking as I realised that I did not have a plan for the following year. My greatest fear was that after all my education I would wind up in a factory like my parents who migrated in the early 1970s from Sāmoa to ensure my siblings and I lived better lives. I did not want to disappoint my parents or make light of their hard work and sacrifices for us. The pressure to make them proud weighed on me heavily. Hopeless, I prayed and asked God to open a door for me.

A couple of weeks later, my English teacher asked if I had considered becoming a teacher? The thought had never crossed my mind, as I did not think I was intelligent enough to be one. He went on to say that during our visit to a local primary school he noticed that I had a natural rapport with the children and knew instantly that I would be a fantastic teacher! He surprised me later, by giving me an application pack for Teachers' College.

If this teacher had not seen the gold in me, and if he had not believed in me, I would have missed out on a career that I absolutely love.

Another teacher who was instrumental in modelling what a good teacher should be like was an associate teacher who mentored me while completing my teaching experience (TE) section at an Intermediate School. The first thing I noticed was that the physical environment reflected the cultural diversity of all the students. The room was bright and welcoming with cultural greetings, borders, projects, karakia or tatalo (prayer) and photos of the students displayed on the walls with descriptions of their culture and family.

The teaching day also reflected the cultural diversity of the class, where the day started and ended with a karakia or tatalo, and during the day a waiata would be sung or sāsā danced, led by the faaluma (leader) calling out the commands. The students knew that they belonged in this space and they thrived. This was due to the teacher, for creating and fostering a culturally inclusive learning space.

Both these teachers greatly influenced my philosophy and style of teaching today, which is strengthened and tied together by my own cultural identity as Sāmoan.

For instance, I've always seen my class as not just family, but as 'āiga. The typical idea of family is that of your immediate nuclear family. But as 'āiga, our family includes our extended family and I have grown up with parents who adopted many kids from Sāmoa and housed many relatives new to New Zealand. So the importance of 'āiga and alofa (love) were ingrained in us from an early age.

This is why my teaching practice is anchored in alofa, as I believe that our students are not going to care about what we're teaching them, until they know that we care about them. I aim to make sure each and every student in my class feels a sense of belonging by developing positive relationships with them, and that enables me to effectively engage them in their learning and their world.

Our classroom is also not just a room, but it is our fale, our home. Our fale is a safe space where we talanoa (talk) and breathe life into our alofa, faaaloalo (respect), and tautua (service), for anyone and everyone - not only the students in my class. Our fale has boundaries and expectations too where we are accountable for looking after our environment, we respect each other, we care about each other's wellbeing and progress so that we can better serve and support each other.

Every day, I know that there is a student sitting in our fale, within our 'āiga who hasn't realised their full potential. This highlights the power of the life-giving words that we can speak each day to seek out the gold and support our students to fulfill their maximum potential.

For me, it took one teacher and one moment to impact me in a way that changed the direction of my life. And this is what I aim to do every day.

I now aim to seek out the gold and potential buried under the insecurities and fears of my own students. I aim to empower my students to believe that they can excel, achieve their goals and dreams in life, while significantly impacting and changing their world for the better.

Often teachers ask me, "Why do the Pasifika students sit, listen, and work for you and not in my class?" Many contribute it to the Pasifika factor - because I am Sāmoan. But the teachers who significantly impacted my life and inspired me were all pālagi! They were good teachers who took the lead to cultivate culturally responsive learning and inclusive environments, through identifying and building upon my personal strengths and potential.

What I've found is that empowering our students is key and I believe this cannot be done without them feeling a sense of belonging in their learning spaces and environment. When they belong and know that we believe in them, it makes it so much easier for the students to believe in themselves. Then, when our students believe in themselves and know what they can achieve, they are able to find an inner strength that will help them for the rest of their life. And the best part is that when they succeed and shine, they give others permission to also succeed and shine, which I am so grateful and blessed to witness.

This is why I love what I do. I'm a proud Sāmoan educator who knows that when my students walk into our fale, they know they are 'āiga. They feel like they belong, their voices are heard and they're empowered to believe in themselves to do great things and go beyond the limits of their own minds and worlds –

Dear Miss,
You told me once, that you had seen me grow, grow from being shy and quiet to a confident young lady - I owe that growth in my life to you.

I can't thank you enough for making your classroom environment incredibly open and unique. I will always remember you for being the most inspiring teacher. I don't think words will ever describe the impact of your 'Class Talks' and their hidden teachings about life morals had on me.

I believe my new way of thinking started when I entered your classroom. Before I entered your class, I had no idea what the words / meanings of goals, determination, aiming higher, striving to be nothing but ambitious, meant. You taught me to dream of any dream and believe in myself.

In those two years, I felt like I had been taught how to plant the foundation of my life, of the endless possibilities that I could eventually become. You always made me believe that I could accomplish anything, and I'm incredibly grateful for that.

Thank you for being one of the BIGGEST impactors and influencers of my life. I wouldn't be who I am without you.

Forever grateful,
A.

(Email from ex-student who was studying at University at the time it was written.)

Niusila Faamanatu-Eteuati

Lecturer at School of Languages and Cultures and Faculty of Humanities and Social Sciences, Victoria University of Wellington
Twenty-three years in Education, two years as Graduate Assistant for Faculty of Education at Victoria University of Wellington, eleven years as Lecturer for Faculty of Education at National University of Sāmoa, Le Papaigalagala, four years as Head of Social Science Department and teacher at Sāmoa College, PhD Education Psychology, MA/MEd SEN, B.SocScie, DipSecSchTchng.

'Tama'ita'i Faiā'oga Sāmoa –
Le Utuga o le Mālamalama ia 'oa!
Sāmoan Woman Educator –
Enriching the Funds of Knowledge!

Mauri mahi, maui ora.
E tautala aso, e iloga taumafaiga.
Through work we prosper.
He waka eke noa.
Tatou te malaga faatasi.
We journey together.
Ehara taku toa, i te toa takitahi.
He toa takitini tōku toa.
My strength is not due to me alone,
but due to the strength of many.
O so'u malosi'aga na fautele mai ē e ou faatufugaga.
Ua ta inu, ua ta malie, ua ta pa'i ai i Vaioletama.

Faatulou atu i le pa'ia ma le mamalu o le 'au faitau,

Ao ni nai motugā'afa mo mātua, faiā'oga, ma fānau.

Faafetaia ma le loto maualalo le avanoa e talatala ai sina faamalosi'au,

Tōmānatu i le tuana'i, o manū e fotua'i ai, a'o se 'upega ne'i maumau.

E mano ma mano fetū ta'iala i folauga o Sāmoa,

A'o le vala'auina faafaiā'oga e a'oa'o atu pea ma le loto ua āto'atoa.

Ua silia nei ma le 20 tausaga o se 'au'aunaga e fia faaasoa,

Le tama'ita'i Sāmoa, e lasi ona faivaalofilima ma lana utugā'oa.

Na ola a'e ma a'otauina lava i Sāmoa le atunu'u pele,

O nai ona matua o ulua'i faiā'oga sa tapu'e ma faalototele.

E inainā le tamā ia Utugaalematemate le Polōfesa o tomai ma silafia,

Afīfī i le tu'umumusu a mā Kueni 'O le poto ma le faaeaina o 'oe lava ia sā'ili'ilia'

Toa o le galuega sa moemiti ia i'u le galuteine e to'aono, ae tasi le tama.

Faamanatu i talanoaga *'E tū le 'āiga teine, o le māopoopoga o so'otaga mafanafana'*.

Le tama'ita'i Sāmoa,

E faalogo ma usita'i, e faamuamua le Atua i lana utugā'oa.

Masalo ai o ni fuafuaga mamao nei a le Māta'isau,

Pe na fetalanoa'ai o latou mauli, a'o ē i le manava o lē na to'alafanau.

Faaigoaina ai 'oe o *'Niusila'* a'o faasikolasipi faafaiā'oga i
fafo le toea'ina,
Pinefaamau o taumafaiga a le tua'ā ma lana foi faaeaea i si
ona 'āiga.
Mai se nu'u faatauvaa, mamao i tuā ma le lē aloa'ia,
A'o le fu'a taualuga lava i matua ma 'āiga o le atamai ia
'ausia.
Le tama'ita'i Sāmoa,
E finafinau, tauivi ma filigā, o Faaaliga o loto e totoa.

Le amataga i ā'oga faifeau, savali i le timuga ma le mugalā,
Faavae o le olaga ma le gagana, o le 'āiga lava ma le falesā.
Misi ā'oga amata ae laa i le tulagalua sa puleā'oga ai tinā ma
tamā,
Faaletonu tamaiti i vasega ua muamua lava 'aina iā 'oe le tā.
Auā e ao ona e tausili, fai 'oe ma faata'ita'iga o le sogasogā,
Le tama'ita'i Sāmoa,
Faamemelo i ai matua, i'oimata o le tuagane, le feagaiga ma
le fai'oa.

Mai lenā olaga tautevateva ma le tau autago,
Taumafai i ā'oga a le nuu, faasolo i Apia ma atunuu i fafo.
Le fiafiaga sili o mātua aso o laugātogi ma faau'uga,
E mitamita tinā, siva faaali le tatau a tamā, a'o tupe ua
faaaogā uma.
O loto ua faagae'etia a'o i Sāmoa, Peretānia, atu Europa ma
Aotearoa,
Talosaga lē utuvā a 'āiga ma ekalesia, o ana lupe faalele i le
vasaloloa.

148

Le tamaʻitaʻi Sāmoa,

Tiu i lou faasinomaga, o au vaogagana lou tofi lenā ia ātoa.

Galue faatinā e tapena faapei o sana lava fanau moni,

Ia amanaʻia soo se tamaitiiti, e lautua i le alofa ma le faamāoni.

Faatusa i le tautai e mataʻalia i matagi ma souā o le gataifale,

Faasafua atu le mālamalama i e atamamai ma tama valevale.

O mātua foi e ao ona lagolago, taʻitaʻi ma talitonuina le faiāʻoga,

E matimati le iloa, ma totō le fatu o le gagana ia ola i lagona.

Na te lavātia foi le faatauemu ma tigā ona o le onosaʻi,

O lelei ma leaga e te amoina pea, seʻia totogo aʻe mālama ma se tali.

E lasi matāʻupu ma suʻesuʻega i le poto salalau lautele,

Tomai i le siʻomiaga, le lalolagi o tagata, o mea e ola ma faafailele.

Mai nei sailiiliga uma na uia e leʻi mūitiiti ai le fiafia i lana gagana Sāmoa,

Le fuiniu ua ifo i le lapalapa, le tautua ua au, le inaʻilau ua sooʻātoa.

E leʻi faafuāveta la ona tauasa mai le vaofilifili ma le tāgutugutu o le pogisā.

Auā na lalagofaatasi ma le tapuaʻiga mai faleoʻo o tuaʻā.

Le tamaʻitaʻi Sāmoa,

E sailimālō ma lavapapale, e finafinau ma le alofa ia tufa atu lana utugā'oa.

O le mau a le tusi 'Faamanatu mai le Matāmatagi,'
'Afuaga o gagana le lotoifale, sosolo atu i tafa o le lalolagi'
Talanoa, faitau, tusitusi, tatalo, pese, faalogo, ia faaosofia
moegāluaga i le Faasāmoa,
Oka se manaia o se tama vaeoso, folafolaga o taumafa alu
ma le ātoa.
Le teine ua talatala fulu mafaufauga i gagana e lua ua tā oso
ai lona iloa,
Filosofia faaleā'oā'oga e matala atili le mafaufau, mausalī ai
ma le mautinoa.
Le tama'ita'i Sāmoa,
E faafeao 'oe e le mālamalama, ma le osaosa o lau
utugā'oa.

Le to'aiga i matagi o le atuvasa ua tuta i nuu manaia lona sa,
E fai 'oe ma fala se'ese'e ae malu ai fanau i vaitau afā.
E taavili pea le lalolagi ma manatu i suiga o le talutalufou,
Ia lē nofoa'i i ou agavaa, aganuu ma lau gagana ia poupou.
O au agatausili e totonugalēmū ai ou so'otaga i le va ma
tagata,
Fai mālū ou faiva ma le tauagafau, o 'anava ia faatausala.
Le tama'ita'i Sāmoa, se ua malie le Papaigalagala,
Lafo ane le taula o le Va'aomanū i Te Wanganui a Tara.

Afai sa ou mafaia i se vaivaiga, o se lu'i lenā mo 'oe,
E alu aso, sau aso e tula'i mai foi e tu taumua i le foe.
Ua na'o se faafanua na lolomiina i lo'u loto ma faatonufolau,

Lufilufi atu ia, auā lou gaseā i se manuia mo fanau.

Muāfetalaiga a Sāmoa *'E iloa le tufuga lima lelei i le soofau'*

Fautuaga teufatu, faatāua lou vala'auina nei tafea i le au.

Faafetaia le Tapa'au i le soifua ma'ema'e ma nafa faatō'aga,

Le moana sausau, a'e i mauga ma ifo vanu ae na iloga ou ala

Le faiā'oga tama'ita'i Sāmoa,

E! Ua malie ō, o galuega ua fua ma faailoa.

Lau faatamasoāliiga, o mo'omo'oga ia mau pea lau utugā'oa.

This *'solo a le faiā'oga'* summarises one's journey as a Sāmoan woman educator from humble beginnings – paddling from an outer Sāmoan village in Aleipata, navigating the immeasurable winds and currents to the whenua o Aotearoa.

It is the dream and prayer of every Sāmoan parent for their daughters to be blessed in education and thrive equipped with the funds of knowledge. This is why, born to Sāmoan Christian parents who were educators, school principals and school inspectors, Niusila was not only a name but a destiny of this tama'ita'i Sāmoa's educational success.

Tīgā ona si'i 'ita i lugā, o le faiā'oga lē aogā.

Folau pea ia ma le manuia i vasa e tele – Soifua!

Whaowhia te kete matauranga -

Fill the basket of knowledge.

Acknowledgements

My amazing husband, Mani, I thank you for believing in me before I ever did, teaching me how to dream and for our two beautiful boys, Mason and Isaia – 'ou te alofa ia te 'oulua, more than you'll ever know and know that this is all for you.

Mum and dad, for all the sacrifices and alofa, teaching us the importance of education and our Sāmoan culture. My 'āiga and friends, your endless support has given me the courage to continue on this writing journey. I am forever grateful for you all.

Emeli Sione, Tapu Misa from e-tangata and Lani Wendt-Young, I am beyond blessed with all your advice and guidance, and I thank you for all that you do for our people while being living examples of what Pasifika supporting Pasifika looks like.

My guardian angels, thank you for your presence, protection and for raising me to be a strong teine Sāmoa like yourselves – I miss you and I hope I have made you all proud.

Finally, to our contributing authors - Telesia Tanoai, Trinity Tauaneai, Rebecca Sa'u, Akenese McCarthy, Sarah McLeod-Venu, Angela Milovale, Tuto'atasi Vailalo, Makerita Feite Tago, Eleanor McLeod, Trisha Daniels-Sopoaga, Vaia'ua'u Pilitati, Sinapi Taeao, Nila Uili, Niusila Faamantu-Eteuati – Faafetai tele lava to every one of you for supporting my mission, entrusting me with your stories and filling the Teine Sāmoa Project space with your beautiful voices.

About the author

Dahlia Malaeulu is a New Zealand-born Sāmoan, with her father Malo Gray originating from the village of Sinamoga and her mother Lagi Gray (née Saletele) from the village of Vaivase tai. Dahlia is married to Mani Malaeulu and is the proud mother of two young boys, Mason and Isaia.

Dahlia is a passionate educator at heart, and in 2019 she released the first books of the 'Mila's My Gagana' series, a set of early Sāmoan language readers (*Malia Shares*, *Lagi Spies* and *Mase's Room*) for pre-school and junior-primary-aged children. The series is a rich literacy resource for all children, families and educators in order to support and develop the learning of basic Gagana Sāmoa (the Sāmoan language).

Ultimately, Dahlia would love to enable tamaiti to confidently and proudly succeed as Pasifika. This is why she would love to see endless options of accessible quality Pasifika stories and resources that reflect our Pasifika values, languages, cultures and most importantly, our tamaiti.

You can find more of her writing at her blog: milasdm.wordpress.com, stay updated via Facebook: @MilasBooks or get in touch via email milasbks@gmail.com

Made in United States
Orlando, FL
09 February 2022

14645528R00093